C000231432

ROLLS-ROYCE PISTON AERO ENGINES
— a designer remembers

A A Rubbra

HISTORICAL SERIES No 16

Published in 1990 by the
Rolls-Royce Heritage Trust
PO Box 31 Derby England

ISBN: 1-872922-00-7

Also published in the series:

Cover: Rolls-Royce Merlin XX

 by Bemrose Security Printing, Derby

CONTENTS

FOREWORD

Over the eighty years and more that Rolls-Royce has been in existence, legions of men and women have made their own individual contributions to the Company's achievements. Some, like Henry Royce himself, or Ernest Hives, are well known by name and their life's work are widely appreciated. Among those less well known - or not even known at all - are a number whose contribution rose above the ordinary to reach heroic proportion. One such was Arthur Rubbra: Rbr.

To suggest that Rbr was little known, or that his achievements were unrecognised, would be nonsense. Indeed, many who worked with him - or just knew him - held him in reverence, and none but the most outstanding engineers in Rolls-Royce have ever risen to become the Company's Technical Director. Equally few have been awarded the CBE for their work. What made Rbr so unique was his quiet nature. In this he was so unlike those who Alec Harvey-Bailey has aptly described as Hives' turbulent barons. Rbr's influence came from the depth of his thought and the logic of his proposals and not through the force of argument. He was utterly self effacing and would invariably deflect praise onto his colleagues, even when the credit truly belonged to himself.

I was privileged to find myself working with Rbr at a very early stage in my career. As a graduate apprentice in 1960 I proposed the establishment of a Rolls-Royce museum, and the Board nominated Rbr to foster the project with me. Although much work was done by us on the project, the Board decided in finality not to proceed with it. Later, the engines we had amassed became the basis for the Rolls-Royce collection in Derby Industrial Museum. Rbr was much involved in its establishment.

It was some years later, after his retirement, that Rbr felt that the work of the Derby Engine Design Office between the wars should be recorded for posterity, and this volume is the outcome of his initiative. When he began writing he had no idea of how or where the end result might be published.

Rbr and I never lost contact with one another, and when the Trust was formed I was more than pleased to see him join, and even more to witness the pleasure he so obviously gained from the events of the Derby Branch. He had lost his wife and the companionship he found in the Trust clearly rekindled earlier interests for him and helped fill a void. It was natural that the Trust should offer to publish his manuscript, and this is it. Sadly, Rbr died long before we could get this book printed. The text called for many illustrations which have proved very difficult to find. A great deal of work had to be put in by Bob Forrester, Richard Haigh, Alec Harvey-Bailey and Dave Piggott in bringing the volume to its present published form, and they have all given their time and energy out of respect for his memory.

Our thanks go too to Lionel Haworth, who grew in stature as a designer under the wing of Rbr. His appreciation of Rbr is included by way of a introduction to the main narrative. Without his pen picture of Rbr, the man, and his achievements, it would be impossible to judge the book in its true light - as an account of Rbr's own achievements over the period.

M H Evans Chairman

January 1990

5

Arthur Alexander Rubbra CBE, BSc, FRAeS, FIMechE.

ARTHUR ALEXANDER RUBBRA

An appreciation by a junior colleague and friend

Mr A A Rubbra CBE BSc FEng RDI FRAeS FIMechE was the last in a succession of great aero engine designers who helped create and sustain the name of Rolls-Royce through two world wars.

Arthur Alexander Rubbra was born on 29 October 1903, the second son of a Northampton watchmaker. He and his brother Edmund, the distinguished British composer, did not have rich parents, and made their way by hard work and by their exceptional talents.

After winning an open scholarship from Northampton school to Bristol University, he travelled between his home and Bristol on his pedal cycle, to share the same benches with two young men, Cyril Lovesey and Ray Dorey, who were also to give lifelong service to Rolls-Royce. Sir Archibald Russell, a contemporary at Bristol, said of Arthur Rubbra that he was "the bright one of the bunch who always got full marks for everything".

Whilst these young men were undergraduates, Henry Royce (R) was busy with his designs at West Wittering, his home and work place near Chichester, and E W Hives (Hs) was beginning to recruit promising graduates into the Derby Experimental Department. After gaining his honours degree, Rubbra was appointed by Hives in July 1925, being preceded by Lovesey (Lov) and followed by Dorey (Dor).

Arthur Rubbra's Bristol nickname had been *Bungie*, and much as schoolboys use master's nicknames, this was still heard in Derby in World War Two; but most colleagues and friends usually respectfully and affectionately called him Rbr. Hives always called him Rub-ra, with the first syllable as in 'rub'; a few contemporaries like Lovesey naturally called him Arthur.

Rbr's first task on joining Rolls-Royce involved getting more power from the Eagle engine, and he was given the opportunity of developing the first Rolls-Royce supercharger, working both in Derby and at the Royal Aircraft Establishment at Farnborough.

In the late 1920s he transferred to design under A J Rowledge (Rg), a highly respected figure in the Industry, who had earlier designed the Napier Lion engine. Whilst Rowledge was working in the Derby design office, A G Elliott (E) was with R at West Wittering. Rg had to sell his proposals to R, giving Rbr opportunities of learning the skills of R at first hand. Rbr always spoke highly of Rg and E, and with deep admiration of the detail design work of R. His praise of Rg, E and R was not just hero worship, but flowed from pure generosity of spirit, allied to a deep understanding of what was good in engineering. He never willingly mentioned his own good work, though he might tell on occasion how his work had turned out badly.

If one could get Rbr to 'open up a little', he would usually say "Well, you see we were up against so and so and eventually we arrived at this:" Out would come his

7

Rolls-Royce works' outing to Calshot for 1929 Schneider Trophy—the party awaiting the coach in Nightingale Road—Ray Dorey on the front row—second from the left and **Rbr** behind and to the left.

pencil, with which he would make a clear, careful, correct, but inartistic sketch[1]. He carefully avoided suppressing initiative but he knew that, without a clear sketch, some people were apt to go away and draw something quite different!

I never met a man who could impart so much information with so few words. He once recommended me to use the principle of a bicycle freewheel and when I confessed I hadn't seen the inside of one, he said "I should go out and buy one then". That is why the starter motor engaging mechanism on the Dart resembles a cycle freewheel!

I have often sat with him in a small, senior design meeting. A cathedral calm prevailed until someone plucked up enough courage to make a suggestion. The source of the interruption would then be calmly surveyed by that intelligent countenance. A kindly look usually, but perhaps slightly pained or tinged with pity. "Yes" he would say, "I've been over that one, but if we did that, so and so would go wrong". I have on occasion hoped that the Earth would open and provide escape from that calm, quiet presence, which was always two jumps ahead. An hour or two of this treatment was definitely bad for the morale. In time one learned to take it and survive, for the pained expression was reserved for chatterboxes and those who did not think. It did not matter who made a good suggestion, the speed of his comprehension was almost uncanny; no need to say anything twice, he had it in a flash.

Institution of Automobile Engineers dinner in March 1933—Rbr is on the extreme right, with Eric Platford 2nd from the right and A. G. Elliott 4th from the right.

After several years of struggling to keep up with his intellect, I was one day asked to come to his office. "Sit down, Lionel" he said quietly, "I only wanted to use you as a sparring partner!" Out came his pencil and the problem on his mind, concerning an

[1] An example of Rbr draughtmanship is shown in figure 58 - a design scheme DES 1580 drawn by Rbr on 4.11.31 and initialled AAR.

9

engine not my responsibility, was explained. Silence. "What do you think, Lionel?". After the discussion I left somewhat elated. The oracle had been consulting me! This was the first of many occasions, when I saw him consulting with others. Although ahead of most people, he was always ready to learn.

E, a masterly designer himself, had a very high opinion of Rbr. I recall an occasion when I was summoned to go with Rbr, to the board room in Nightingale Road, to explain to E my progress in re-designing the front end of the Dart. After perhaps an hour, it could be seen that, although E was interested, he was running out of time. Turning to Rbr he asked his opinion. "I have no doubt" said Rbr, "that Lionel is right; my only doubt is whether we have time to do it". He did not mention his considerable contribution to the work. I got all the credit. One could see E's mind jump to a conclusion. "In that case" said E, "we must make time". One sentence from Rbr had been enough to settle a major decision. I went back to work thinking how marvellous it was to work for men of such integrity and generosity of spirit whose only concern was to get the engineering right at the design stage. Lesser men would have grumbled that I was at risk of delaying the programme.

Rbr's quietly patient approach was extended to all ranks in his search for the best solution, and in over 40 years I can recall only two occasions when he lost his temper! He had a well developed sense of humour. He loved to listen to amusing stories concerning people we all knew, and would laugh as heartily as anyone. Often, he would tell a good story himself. It seems that Rg, when he did not like a proposal by Sir Henry, did not say so, but went away dutifully and had it drawn out, along with several alternatives, including his own preferred scheme. The latter would be diffidently shown last after the old man was seen to be dissatisfied with all the others. "The ruse always worked", said Rbr, with a quiet amused smile spreading over his face. I never told him

Dr Gordon Mitchell, son of R. J. Mitchell, Arthur Rubbra CBE and John Waghorn, son of H. R. D. Waghorn, the 1929 winner, at the 1981 50th Anniversary Celebrations of the Schneider Trophy at Calshot Spit.

10

that Ralph Shire and I used to practice a similar technique on him, but I suspect he had twigged it anyway.

Rbr had great tenacity and would never leave a problem 'up in the air'. If the end of the day brought no satisfying solution, one could lay odds that, in spite of his many other preoccupations, he would be in the next morning with ideas that would solve the problem or at least take it a stage further.

After the death of Sir Henry, E became the Company's Chief Designer, and in 1934 Rbr was appointed deputy to Colonel Barrington (Bn), Chief Designer, Aero Engines. Rbr was probably the best design engineer in the Company in the late 1930s. Although he did not match the talents of E as a designer draughtsman, he had had a better training in engineering science. All Rbr's training at Bristol and in Derby was now to be put to the test.

With war approaching, Rbr, Lov and Stanley Hooker (SGH) headed the team, which kept the Merlin just ahead of the German engines. SGH had joined the company in 1938 and his brilliant academic career had equipped him to master quickly the problems of supercharging. E made his contribution to the design work; but it required a younger man to rise to the supreme challenge, and there is no doubt that Rbr carried the heat and burden of piston engine design in Derby from before 1935, throughout the war and into the peace, to the end of the civil Merlin phase and beyond.

In 1943 Rolls-Royce acquired control of the Northern Factories of the Rover Company, developing Whittle engines at Barnoldswick. SGH went there as Chief Engineer, and from that time on, Rbr increasingly shared responsibility for turbine design work.

He made a great contribution to the turbo-props, the Trent, Clyde, Dart and Tyne; and also to the later marks of the Derwent, Nene, Avon, Conway and to other post-war engines; but his greatest work was undoubtedly the Merlin, without which there would have been no Hurricane, Spitfire, Lancaster or Mosquito, and no successful outcome to the Battle of Britain. Rbr, Lov, SGH and their teams took the Merlin from 1,000 hp at the outbreak of war to over 2,000 by its end, on basically the same crankshaft, connecting rods and pistons, by using the high pressure and density of the cylinder charge, provided by the blowers and intercoolers, of ever increasing size.

The awesome responsibility and workload was crippling, and left its mark on Rbr. After the war he suffered from insomnia, which forced him, occasionally, to have to rest. I asked him once if the cause was known. "The war" he said, "I destroyed my health during the war; working all day around the boards and reading papers most of the night".

In addition to the Merlin, he was, of course, responsible during the war for the Griffon and the last piston engine to be made in Derby - the 24-cylinder sleeve valve Eagle, which was overtaken by the gas turbine.

After becoming Deputy Chief Engineer in 1951 he was involved in all the Company's aero projects. In 1954 he was appointed Technical Director responsible for all forms of transportation including cars. He moved his office to the Old Hall, Littleover, to head up the advanced research organisation set up by Lord Hives. It worked on new materials and engineering concepts. Nuclear work came along and Rolls-Royce and Associates was founded in 1959, with Rbr as deputy chairman until 1966.

He was honoured by the award of the CBE in 1961, served on many committees in aerospace, and was at one time a governor of Lanchester College. He was also a director of several other companies. He became Chief Technical Adviser to Rolls-Royce in 1966 and retired from full time work in 1968, remaining a consultant until his total service to the Company had exceeded half a century.

The Royal Aeronautical Society awarded him the highest honour it can bestow, its Gold Medal, in 1969 "for outstanding contributions over many years in the whole field of aircraft propulsion".

He was elected a Royal Designer for Industry in 1977 and a Fellow of the Fellowship of Engineering in 1980. In his retirement, the well-deserved rest had a beneficial effect except for the period of the illness of his wife, who died in 1979. Though later a little frail he continued in good health and spirits and with a clear mind up to the end. Fond of classical music, he spent much time listening to his favourite composers. He died on 24 November 1982 at the age of 79.

To my mind, the big names in Rolls-Royce aero engine design, after Sir Henry Royce, were Rg, E, and Rbr. In that field he was our last link with those who sustained the Magic of the Name through World War One and Two, by excellence in design. Because of his self-effacing ways, I hold Rbr to be one of those great men, who in the spirit of Gray's Elegy, have not had their share of praise for their achievements - a gentle giant!

Lionel Haworth
Bristol
14 December 1982.

ROLLS-ROYCE PISTON AERO ENGINES

— a designer remembers

I joined the Company in July 1925 as an assistant aero engine tester in the Experimental Department. At that time the Company had started to build up an engineering staff recruited from university graduates and had already taken on A C Lovesey from Bristol University where I also received my engineering training and degree.

There was no formal training scheme within the Company for such graduates at that time, as had been established by the Daimler Company where previously I had unsuccessfully applied as a graduate trainee. There was, however, a formal training scheme for premium apprentices and also for trade apprentices.

At that time the total employment of the Company was of the order of 3000, the General Manager in Derby was A Wormald (Wor) and in charge of the Experimental Department was E W Hives (Hs). This department was closed off from the rest of the works in Nightingale Road and could only be entered from two gates manned by watchmen whose duty it was to see that no-one, apart from members of the department, was allowed to enter without an appropriate permit. The reason for this arrangement

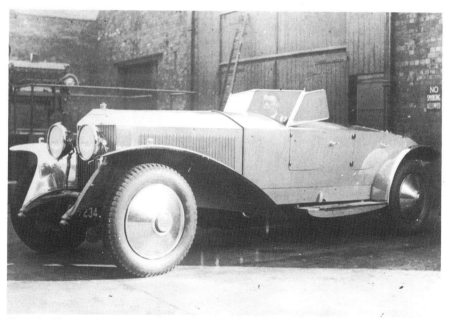

Figure 1   The experimental sports model (16 EX) based on the Phantom 1 with A. J. Lidsey (Lid) at the wheel.

13

was to prevent advance knowledge of new car models, being worked on in the department, from reaching the Press and affecting the sales of current models. At this time the 'New Phantom' series[2] of cars was being introduced to replace the Silver Ghost. The new chassis mark numbers were preceded by the letters EAC which were said to mean 'Eastern Armoured Car'.

To lend support to this, sheets of what purported to be armour plate labelled with the same letters writ large, were stacked just beyond the watchman's hut, all this being done to disguise the fact that a replacement for the Silver Ghost was being worked.

I recall seeing a Phantom I car with a very pretty boat-shaped open tourer body painted in light blue. It was an experimental sports model (16 EX) in which the Company were trying to interest the Prince of Wales (1).

[2] The Phantom I as we know it, was the 'New Phantom' when introduced. Only with the launch of the Phantom II did it become known as the Phantom I.

THE EARLY AERO ENGINES

At this time the production of aircraft engines was at quite a low ebb, an order for the Condor III engines being nearly completed. The Condor (2) was an enlarged version of the Eagle, rated at 650 hp and powered the Hawker Horsley aircraft. In 1923 A J Rowledge (Rg) who had been responsible for the design of the Napier Lion engine, was taken on as Assistant Chief Engineer to Henry Royce (R) and had established a small design office in Derby mainly to deal with aero engine work. His first task was a revision of the earlier Condor design to improve its power rating and to reduce its basic frontal area in the interests of reduced drag. This involved the use of lead-bronze bearings, reducing the overall height of the cylinders relative to the crankshaft centre-line, and the provision of a spur reduction gear, instead of an epicyclic, to place the propeller shaft at roughly the centre of the frontal area. This became the Condor III (3).The lead-bronze was Kelmet, consisting of 24% lead, 6.5% tin and the balance copper, but production engines used larger white metal bearings, Kelmet proving unsuccessful on test.

Another task he undertook at this time was a design of a servo assisted brake system (4) for the Rolls-Royce car. This consisted basically of a low speed shaft driven from the gearbox on which was mounted a friction clutch, the torque from which, when

Figure 2   Rolls-Royce Condor 1A.

15

engaged by the brake pedal, multiplied the load transmitted to the brake shoes. This proved to be a very successful system and was used largely unaltered on all subsequent models right up to the Silver Cloud and Bentley 'S' series.

It had a minor fault that in changing direction from forward to reverse, or vice versa, there was a temporary loss of servo assistance due to slack in the system until the car had moved a short distance, and this could be embarrassing when manoeuvring the car in a confined space or on the edge of a sharp drop.

In addition to the above work, designs had been completed for an exhaust turbine driven supercharger for application to a Condor III (**5**). The supercharger unit was placed in the 'V' between the two cylinder banks and, because of the restriction on rotor diameter imposed by this, supercharging was carried out in two stages. Aftercoolers were also provided between the supercharger outlets and the induction manifolds; these were mounted at the front and were air-cooled through forward-facing ducts. The main dimensions for this unit were supplied by the Royal Aircraft Establishment (RAE), Farnborough, who had already had an exhaust-driven supercharger unit designed for the Napier Lion engine and wanted to extend flying experience to higher powers. The Condor application must have been the first aero application of two-stage supercharging, together with aftercooling, and this was to be repeated on the Merlin much later on in the 1940s, although with a gear-driven supercharger. I witnessed the acceptance tests of this engine before it was shipped to Farnborough for high altitude test bed calibration and flight tests.

Figure 3   Rolls-Royce Condor III.

16

Figure 4 Servo assisted brake system for a 40/50 Phantom II.

The full throttle power on the ground was of course considerably reduced because of the restriction imposed by the turbine on the exhaust. The whole of the exhaust manifold system and the turbine casing glowed a bright cherry red and was an awe-inspiring sight for the testers and fitters who had congregated round the test bed to see the first run.

The following is a quotation from a J Ellor[3] memo on the position of the subsequent engine testing at the RAE, Farnborough

Condor with exhaust-driven supercharger

'The position of this engine is somewhat disappointing in that it has not been in the air; a good deal of test bed running has been carried out and useful information gained comparing the same engine normally aspirated and supercharged.

The fuel consumption with the supercharger fitted is slightly less than when normally aspirated, but the bhp developed is down at the normal induction pipe pressure. Tests on the effect of back pressure show that up to the pressure of 6 lb/sq in, the fall off in bhp is 1.6% per lb. An examination of the results obtained indicate a difference in the effect of induction pipe pressures between the two systems of supercharging. I propose to detail these effects at a later date as they may supply interesting data.

[3] J Ellor was Farnborough's supercharging expert up to 1928 and then by agreement between RAE and Rolls-Royce, he joined the Company and took the reference Lr.

17

An RAE report is being prepared on the whole of the development work up to date including the tests and modifications to supercharger. As designed, the two-stage unit is a little less efficient than the single-stage type'.

Work on this project was dropped in accordance with a ruling from the Air Ministry.

Figure 5   Rolls-Royce turbocharged Condor V.

THE KESTREL AND EAGLE XVI

Two other projects were also in hand at this time, one of which was being handled at Derby and the other at West Wittering. The first of these was the 'F' engine later to be known as the Kestrel, and this had been prompted by the success of the Curtiss D 12 liquid-cooled engine in the USA (6). This engine used aluminium cylinder blocks with steel liners instead of separate steel cylinders with welded-on jackets, a construction which considerably improved the beam stiffness of the crankcase and the ability to use higher rpm and powers without crankcase trouble. Work on the 'F' engine was further spurred on by the purchase, by the Fairey Company, of a number of Curtiss D 12 engines for installation in the Fairey Fox, a day bomber with improved lines and performance, resulting from the use of this engine.

The other project, being handled at West Wittering, was a much more ambitious one of about the same power as the 'F'. Known as the Eagle XVI (7), it had 16 cylinders arranged in 4 banks of 4 in 'X' form. This was the power plant favoured by Henry Royce and for this reason it was pushed slightly ahead of the 'F'.

While these two projects were going through the design and manufacturing stages, the testing staff under Tom Warwick were given the task of seeing what improved performance could be wrung out of the Eagle IX (8) by changes in compression ratio and valve timing, etc. This proved to be rather an unprofitable exercise because the

Figure 6   Curtiss D-12-D liquid-cooled engine.

19

Figure 7 Rolls-Royce Eagle XVI.

limitations imposed by the mechanical construction of the engine prevented the use of generally higher rpms.

Although the Eagle IX was nominally rated at 360 hp, there was little or no margin in the rating to allow for small discrepancies between engines.

It was common practice for testers to inject a syringe full of Castrol R oil into the carburettor intakes during the taking of a power curve when the engine was slightly short of power and the AID representative was not looking. This practice usually ensured a pound or two extra on the Froude brake scale pan, by reducing the effect of piston friction.

There was one more development on the Eagle which was being dealt with at this time, and that was the provision of a two-speed propeller reduction gear, with the objective of giving more power for take-off by the use of higher engine rpm.

The Eagle was already provided with a compound epicyclic reduction gear (9) with a friction clutch to hold the fixed sun gear, and it was therefore a fairly simple matter to convert the design of such a gear to give alternative reduction ratios by the introduction of a second sun gear for the primary train and an additional clutch to hold this (10). The clutches were brought into operation by a pressure plate provided with helical teeth on its periphery, which was rotated to engage either clutch by means of a spring-loaded toggle mechanism (11). The operation of this mechanism was obtained by diverting the scavenge oil through an operating cylinder by means of a

20

pilot-operated valve (**11A**), and it is interesting to note that this particular system was again used successfully to operate the two-speed supercharger drive on the Merlin.

Some trouble was at first experienced with clutch slipping (**12**) and this was eventually attributed to the clutch pressure plate moving slightly off centre due to a single point loading from the operating mechanism. The latter was therefore provided with two diametrically opposite loading points which were operated through a bevel differential unit as used on the car brake equaliser system, and this cured the trouble.

As a further precaution I was asked to find out what safety factor there was against slipping under full load. This proved to be quite a simple matter by pulling through a spring balance against the toggle load until a momentary slip occurred and noting the spring balance reading. This caused some consternation on the other test beds when the engine was heard to be racing away, although this caused no harm in fact. The margin against slipping proved to be sufficient.

The results of the ensuing flight tests showed the advantages of such a gear to be marginal, the pilot preferring to leave the gear in low all the time, and the advantages of a two-speed gear were not to be raised again, but for somewhat different reasons, until late in the development of the Griffon for a carrier aircraft.

Reverting to the Eagle XVI 'X' engine, because of the cylinder arrangement the normal method of engine mount by side bearers could not be used. The engine was therefore carried by two strong points at the crankcase sides about half way along, with a further strong point in the top 'V' (**13**). From these strong points three triangulated tubular frames were to be taken back to four strong points on the aircraft

Figure 8 Rolls-Royce Eagle IX with two twin-choke carburettors.

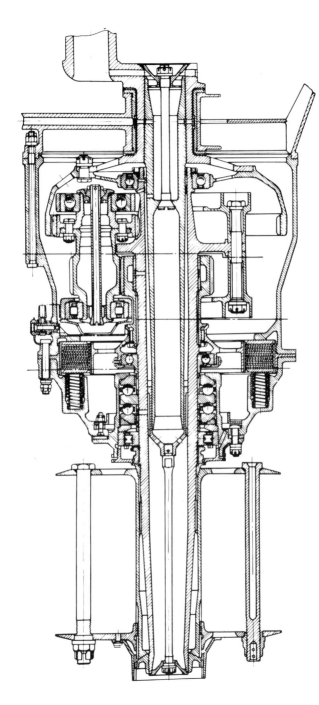

Figure 9 Rolls-Royce Eagle epicyclic reduction gear.

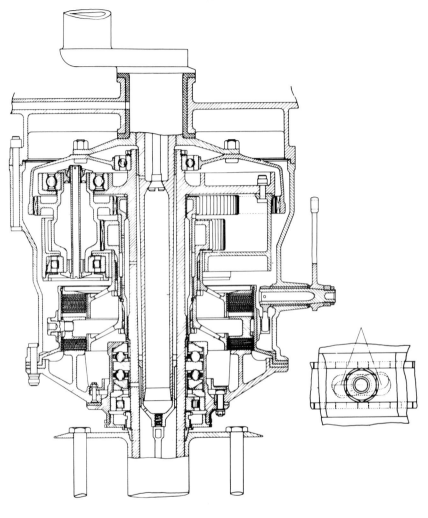

Figure 10 Rolls-Royce Eagle XV two-speed epicyclic reduction gear.

23

bulkhead. A similar mounting was to be successfully used much later on for the Dart prop-jet engine. For the test bed the usual mounting of side rails and pedestals had to be abandoned, and a strong structure of steel plate was erected to provide the equivalent of the aircraft bulkhead to which the tubular frames were attached. There was some apprehension among the testing staff over the use of such an overhung mounting, but provided the test bed couplings were well balanced the engine ran quite steadily.

The problem of anchoring four pistons to a common split big end was side-stepped by the use of separate blade/fork rods for the top and bottom banks mounted side by side on the crankpin.

This meant, of course, that the cylinder centres had to be staggered to allow for this and the cylinder blocks were not therefore common. The four valve cylinder heads were penthouse roof in shape, the valves being operated by a central camshaft through rockers. The 4-throw crankshaft was of the zig-zag type, ie throws 2 and 3 were opposite in the interests of reducing main bearing inertia loads. This proved to be very effective and no trouble was experienced with the white metal bearings.

Both this engine and the 'F' were designed to be fitted with a gear-driven supercharger, this unit being mainly common to both engines except for the manifold offtakes from the delivery volute. The carburettor was carried on the suction side of the supercharger and this proved to be a great advantage in improving the mixture distribution of the cylinders and in reducing the temperature of compression due to the effects of fuel evaporation. This same principle was followed throughout the development of the Company's piston engines and was found to be a great advantage during World War II, when the German engines using direct fuel injection into the cylinder head, did not reap the advantage of reduced charge temperatures.

The supercharger itself was provided with a double entry eye to the impeller which was of the 'open' type, ie, there was no disc to assist the carrying of the blades from the hub. The impeller was therefore very vulnerable to blade failure from vibration, particularly under surging conditions. It was made from forged aluminium. The principle of a double entry eye as a means of keeping down the overall dimensions of the unit was again to be used on the 'R' engine later on, and of course on the Whittle turbojet engine. In the case of the Eagle and 'F', the eye was fitted with static swirl vanes cast in position with the objective of reducing the shock of entry into the impeller, and a vaned diffuser was also provided.

The impeller was fitted with plain white metal bearings and was driven via a spring drive from the crankshaft through three layshafts arranged to give a balanced drive through centrifugally operated friction clutches. The impeller bearings were therefore not subjected to either gear or thrust loads and they gave no trouble although the speed of rotation was high.

Early running of both the Eagle XVI and the following 'F' engine was made without the supercharger and with a temporary rigged-up induction system, the latter presenting considerable difficulty in the case of the Eagle due to poor distribution of the fuel.

Although the Eagle eventually performed quite well on the test bed when fitted with its intended supercharger and carburettor, its reception by the aircraft industry was not enthusiastic mainly because of the effect on the pilots' view when installed in the typical single engine fighter of the day. This eventually led to its abandonment in favour of the 'F', although not before a larger version known as the Eagle XX was worked on at West Wittering but finally abandoned.

It is interesting to note, however, that the cross form of engine was to reappear later on in the 24-cylinder Vulture and Exe engines, and these will be dealt with later on.

24

B.B. 496A (20H) (D.A. 652 20-3-24) J.R.D.

EXPERIMENTAL REPORT.　　　　　Expl. No.　　　　REF: ...W/L.G.7.10.24.

To R. from Hs.
c. to CJ.　AJ.
c. to RG.　E.
c. to BY.　Woy.

.H. EAGLE XV.

An Eagle XV. engine is fitted to a Fairey 3D. type
seaplane.　　The engine has been run up on the ground with a
propeller fitted.

The machine has not been flown however, because they
have had trouble with the clutch for the high speed gear
slipping.

The R.P.M. of the engine on the ground were :-
1520 when on the high gear.
1800 " " " low ".

The slipping occurred at full throttle and the engine raced
away for about half a second at 5 min. intervals.

When the gear was examined it was found that the
plates for the high speed clutch were badly buckled.　This
has been brought about by the slipping.

We shall be running another Eagle XV. fitted with a
2-speed gear on the test bench tomorrow and propose to measure
what margin we have on the spring pressure when running at the
speeds of this engine in the machine.　　If we increase the
spring pressure we shall increase the lag when changing gear.

　　　　　　　　　　　　　　　　　Hs.

Figure 12　Memo from Hs reporting slippage of the clutch in the high speed gear.

When the first 'F' engine (14) appeared on the test bed with its shiny aluminium cylinder blocks it caused a great deal of excitement among the testing staff because of its small size in relation to its rated power compared with that we had been used to seeing. As in the case of the Eagle XVI the supercharger was not fitted to begin with and a temporary induction system was fitted up from two Eagle IX carburetters mounted at the sides and delivering mixture via induction pipes crossing over the top of the rocker covers to the inlet manifolds in the 'V'. This arrangement was a nuisance to the testing staff because it meant removal of the induction system for removal of the rocker covers in order to carry out tappet inspection, etc.

The first run was hardly a success as it would only fire on the end cylinders and the engine was promptly sent back to the shop for investigation, having established that the valve timing was correct according to the crankshaft markings. It was soon found however that there had been a slight error in the drawing office, the firing order for the crankshaft being 1 4 2 6 3 5 while that for the camshafts was 1 5 3 6 2 4. The crankshaft timing marks only referred to the end cylinders which was the reason why this error was not discovered on the test bed.

However, the experimental shop night shift soon had us running properly by slicing up the hollow camshafts into six pieces and pinning them to a central shaft in the correct firing order.

The cylinder blocks on these early engines were of the 'dry liner' type inserted with an interference fit and, to facilitate coring the jacket, spaces were provided with large openings down the sides which had to be closed with sheet metal aluminium covers held on with a multitude of screws (14). It was difficult to make these water-tight, and furthermore considerable trouble was experienced with piston seizures which were put down to poor cooling arising from the use of dry liners.

At about this time also, news reached the company that the Curtiss people had had similar trouble with the liquid-cooled 'V' engine that they were developing, the design of which had been based on the early Hispano Suiza engine which also had dry liners; they were also in trouble with piston seizures and were changing over to a wet liner construction.

This was based on a mixture between the original Hispano Suiza arrangement and the Napier Lion system. In this case the cylinder liner had a blind end and was screwed into the cylinder head and pulled down against the carefully machined face of the cylinder head to form what was known as a 'poultice' head. In this form of head, in order to get good heat transfer from the liner head to the head casting it is important to match these two faces accurately with a good finish, and in order to ensure this good contact an additional stud was provided in the space between the four valve ports. This stud, being in one piece with the liner end, was tightened up after the main screwing-in operation of the liner had been made. This construction meant that the valve seatings provided in the blind end of the liner had to be machined in situ after the liner had been screwed into its final position. Provision had also to be made for an adaptor for the sparking plug which crossed through the screw thread between liner and head and sealed off any possible leaks through the inevitable clearances in the screw thread. These adaptors were made in duralumin. It will be evident from the foregoing that the replacement of a liner, due to wear or damage, or trouble with the valve seatings, was a major and costly operation and because of this and its effect, generally, on engine servicing, it was decided not to follow this construction. The liners themselves were also more costly to produce due to the blind end and integral stud.

Figure 13 Rolls-Royce Eagle XVI—showing the conical engine mounts.

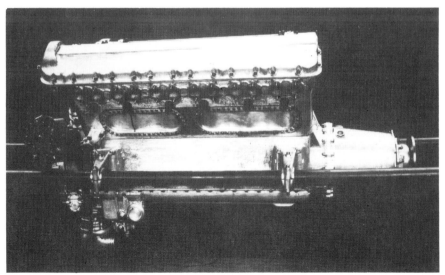

Figure 14 The first Rolls-Royce 'F' engine.

A rather daring design (15) was therefore produced using wet liners in which the liners were introduced through the bores at the bottom of the cylinder block skirt, and making a joint with the cylinder head through a soft washer at their top ends. As far as the cylinder block casting was concerned this meant that the jacket space was completely open for coring purposes from the bottom and therefore no separate covers were required for this purpose.

The cylinder block was held down by means of long studs tapped deeply into the crankcase main bearing panels and passing through tubes in the jacket spaces (spun into position after the manner of steam boiler tubes) through to the top deck, the bolt load being transmitted to the top joint face of the head through the port sides which were thickened up locally for this purpose. The liners themselves were provided with flanges top and bottom, the top one making the cylinder head joint and the bottom one sitting on the crankcase deck.

It is evident that in order to make a good head joint that would resist combustion chamber explosion pressures, it was necessary to have sufficient bolt load and also to

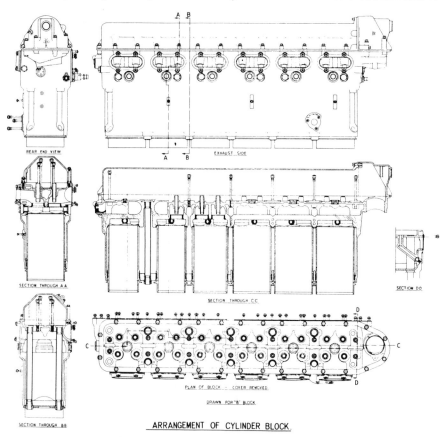

ARRANGEMENT OF CYLINDER BLOCK.

Figure 15 Wet lined cylinder blocks of Rolls-Royce Kestrel engine.

make the liner dimensions between flanges for any one set per block to very close tolerances, and likewise the depth of bore for the liner seatings at the cylinder head. Where the liner passed through the bore at the base of the cylinder skirt it was necessary to provide a sliding joint to allow for relative expansion of liner and block, and this was done by means of a form of rubber ring. The great virtue of this arrangement was, of course, the improved liner cooling achieved, and certainly after its adoption the problem of piston seizures largely disappeared, although there were many other problems to be solved such as getting the required accuracy of manufacture referred to above. The general practice adopted was to select a batch of six liners per block all with dimensions between flanges to very close tolerances with one another.

When the main components of the engine had been demonstrated as satisfactory the supercharger was fitted using a moderate step-up gear ratio of around 6:1 as there were fears that the higher ratio available - about 10:1 - would be a bit too much for a start. The engine ran quite well with good mixture distribution, but the supercharger only succeeded in reducing the normally aspirated inlet manifold depression by about half.

The lower drive gear ratio had obviously reduced the flow capacity of the supercharger, but it was felt that apart from this there was something radically wrong with the supercharger design. Hs therefore packed the writer off to Farnborough, where a test rig existed for measuring supercharger characteristics, together with the offending apparatus in a packing case.

These tests indicated a maximum efficiency of around 37% and Ellor, who was then in charge of supercharger work at Farnborough, was asked to find the reasons for the low efficiency and to suggest the necessary design modifications needed to put the job right.

The two main features considered to be at fault were:
(1) Choking of the inlet due to the fixed swirl vanes and the effect of the opposing streams entering the open impeller blades.
(2) Wrong diffuser vane angles together with much too rapid expansion in the vanes and badly arranged offtakes from the outer volute casing.

The new design proposed consisted of a single entry eye with an entry volute to give swirl to the air entering the impeller in the direction of rotation of the latter, and straight outlet diffuser vanes at a sharper angle.

The new components for this were immediately put in hand and on rig test gave a much improved efficiency of the order of 60%.

Further changes introduced were:
(1) Impeller vanes supported by a one-piece disc up to the periphery with well radiused entry at the hub.
(2) Curved diffuser vanes to give a still slower expansion rate.

The effect of (1) was to reduce the effect of vibration on the impeller blades, to reduce leakage, and to reduce entry losses at the impeller hub, and (2) to improve the diffuser efficiency, and the nett result on the supercharger performance of these changes was to bring the efficiency up to the 70% region. (**16, 17**)

It was also realised that it would be necessary to have our own test rig rather than rely on this work being done at Farnborough, and a suitable rig was therefore put in hand in the 'Bumper' test house. For this the supercharger casing was mounted on a shaft carried on rollers with an arm and scale pan similar to a Froude brake, so that the input torque could be readily measured. It was necessary, of course, to make sure that the air inlets and outlets were balanced or axial in direction.To drive the unit an

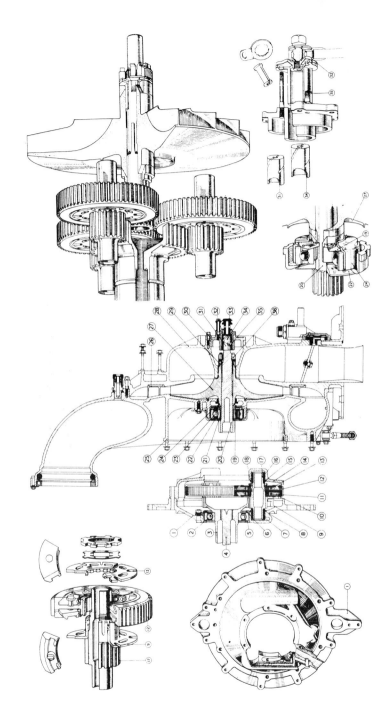

Figure 16 Rolls-Royce Kestrel supercharger and it's gearing—the finally developed version.

30

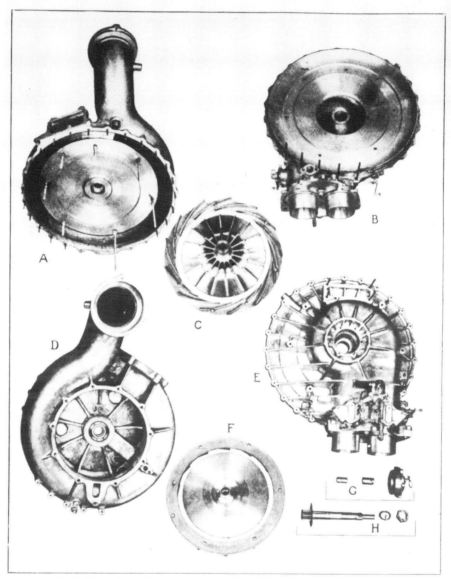

Figure 17   Rolls-Royce Kestrel (I, II and III) supercharger components.

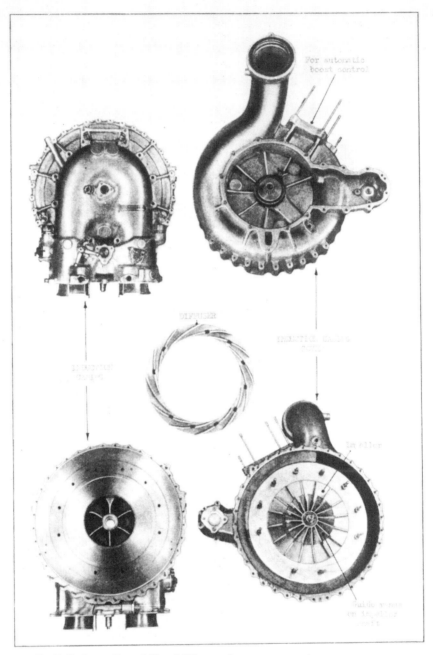

Figure 18   Rolls-Royce Kestrel (V and VI) supercharger components.

old 40/50 engine[4] was used which was rather apt to oil up its plugs on light load. The carburettor was also fitted to the supercharger so that any losses there could be assessed, and the carburettor side intakes equipped with large capacity drums fitted with variable throttles so that varying altitude conditions could be reproduced within the drum. The air mass flow was measured at the outlet by a venturi which had been calibrated at Farnborough.

While all this development work was going on, running had continued on the engine naturally aspirated and eventually the proper carburettor system was fitted. This consisted of two twin choke carburetters (19) carried off the inlet manifolds in the 'V', and joined with a common air intake duct, the entry to which was a vertical stack pipe protruding through the top of the nacelle cowling.

The carburettor (20) float chambers were arranged to be concentric with the main jet so as to avoid acceleration effects, and mixture control was obtained by means of a variable orifice. The whole system was very neatly tucked into the 'V' but by the same token was somewhat inaccessible as also were the sparking plugs on the inlet sides. For this reason the initial development work on the carburettors was carried out by A C Lovesey (Lov) on a special engine which had one cylinder block removed, this factor improving accessibility to all those features which required frequent change.

One other feature which was added early on was a propeller reduction gear (21) to give improved propeller efficiency and to place the propeller at the centre of area of the engine profile viewed from the front. The gear was modelled on the Condor III version but introduced a new feature using a single row deep groove ball bearing to control the axial position of the pinion, the outer tracks of the main roller bearings being without shoulders. This feature was insisted on by Henry Royce because he was afraid the spline friction in the coupling shaft from the crankshaft to pinion would overload any shoulders provided on the roller bearings for end location purposes. This feature worked very well, but was found to be unnecessary on later engines such as the Merlin, where it was found that shoulders provided on the main roller bearings were quite capable of dealing with any axial load arising from spline friction.

The proportions of the gear as designed proved sufficient to cater for the requirements of alternative ratios and subsequent increases in power as the engine was developed by appropriate changes in tooth profiles and increasing the face width of the gears to the maximum permitted by the casings. In common with earlier engines the Kestrel was provided with a spring drive (22) from the rear end of the crankshaft to drive camshafts, magnetos and other auxiliaries including oil and water pumps.

For this purpose the bore of No 7 journal was provided with internal castellations to drive a highly stressed torsion shaft which acted as a spring and was itself splined into an outer shaft which carried the main bevel driving gear. This provided an extremely simple drive with characteristics which would provide wide variations in spring rating by simple dimensional changes, and over-stressing of the torsion shaft was prevented by providing the forward end of the outer shaft with castellations engaging those within the crankshaft but having some 6° of rotational slack within them.

Torsional damping was provided by means of a spring loaded friction plate acting between the crankshaft and the end of the torsion shaft, but this was unnecessary when a supercharger was fitted (23). Even with these precautions service troubles arose in the camshaft drives due to the feedback of torque reversal from the camshafts themselves and it was found necessary to

[4] an old 40/50 refers to a Silver Ghost engine.

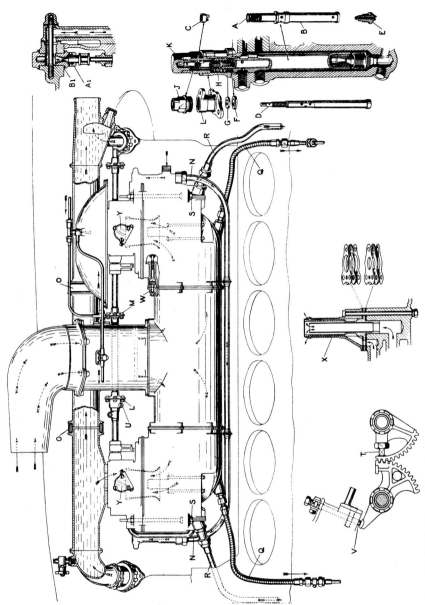

Figure 19 Rolls-Royce Kestrel carburettor installation (naturally aspirated).

34

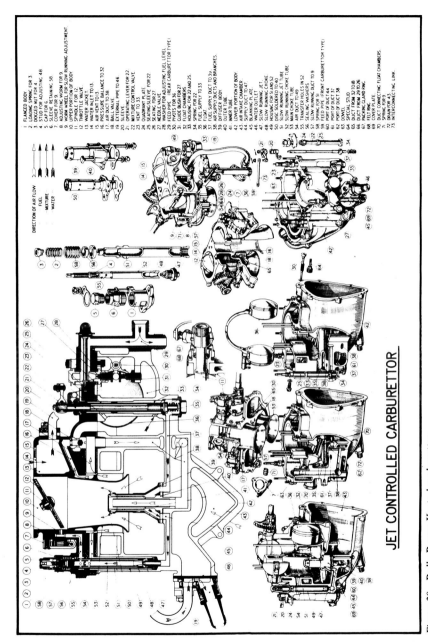

KEY:

1 FLANGED BODY
2 LOADING SPRING FOR 3
3 DOGGED NUT FOR 4
4 STUD FOR ADJUSTING 48
5 CAP FOR 6
6 SLEEVE RETAINING 58
7 COVER FOR 9
8 ADJUSTING WORM FOR 9
9 WORM WHEEL FOR SLOW RUNNING ADJUSTMENT
10 UPPER PORTION OF BODY
11 SPINDLE FOR 12
12 THROTTLE VALVE
13 WATER JACKET
14 WATER INLET TO 13
15 AIR VENT TO 13
16 PRESSURE BALANCE TO 52
17 AIR DUCT TO 38
18 BALL VALVE
19 EXTERNAL PIPE TO 46
20 SLEEVE
21 OPERATING LEVER FOR 22
22 MIXTURE CONTROL VALVE
23 VENT TO 33
24 QUADRANT PLATE
25 SEATING SLEEVE FOR 22
26 SEATING FOR 27
27 NEEDLE VALVE
28 WASHER FOR ADJUSTING FUEL LEVEL
29 FEED PIPE (REAR CARBURETTOR TYPE)
30 PIVOT FOR 96
31 GUIDE BUSH FOR 27
32 FLOAT CHAMBERS
33 HOUSING FOR 22 AND 25
34 SPRING FOR 22
35 FUEL SUPPLY TO 33
36 FLOAT
37 FUEL SUPPLY DUCT TO 39
38 AIR SUPPLY DUCTS AND BRANCHES
39 DIFFUSER BODY
40 OUTER TUBE
41 WATER TUBE
42 LOWER PORTION OF BODY
43 AIR INTAKE CHAMBER
44 SUPPLY DUCT TO 47
45 BLANKING PLATE
46 WATER OUTLET
47 SLOW RUNNING JET
48 SLOW RUNNING CHOKE
49 HOUSING FOR 54 AND 52
50 DISC SOLDERED TO 40
51 SLOW RUNNING JET TUBE
52 SLOW RUNNING CHOKE TUBE
53 MAIN CHOKE TUBE
54 AIR DUCT TO 49
55 TRANSFER HOLES IN 52
56 SEALING WASHERS
57 SLOW RUNNING DUCT TO 9
58 SPRING FOR 51
59 FEED PIPE (FRONT CARBURETTOR TYPE)
60 PORT OF DUCT 37
61 PORT OF DUCT 38
62 PORT OF DUCT 38
63 DOWEL
64 SPECIAL STUD
65 DUCT FROM 32 TO 8
66 DUCT FROM 29 TO 26
67 PACKING GLAND RING
68 FELT RING
69 COVER PLATE
70 DUCT CONNECTING FLOAT CHAMBERS
71 SPRING FOR 9
72 DRAIN FOR 43
73 INTERCONNECTING LINK.

DIRECTION OF AIR FLOW
FUEL
MIXTURE
WATER

JET CONTROLLED CARBURETTOR

Figure 20 Rolls-Royce Kestrel carburettor.

35

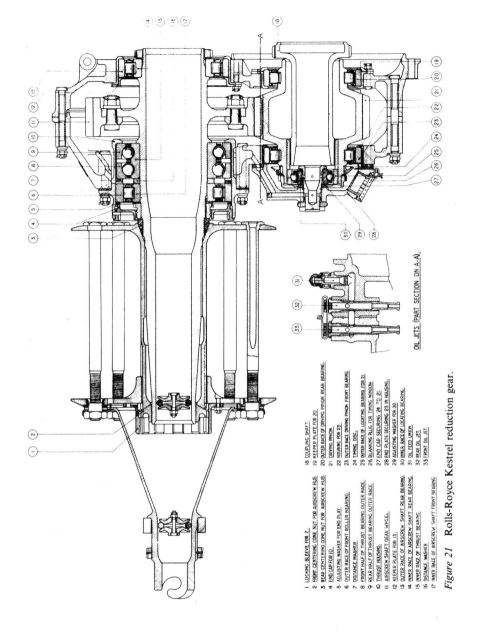

1 LOCKING SLEEVE FOR 2.
2 FRONT CENTERING CONE NUT FOR AIRSCREW HUB.
3 REAR CENTERING CONE NUT FOR AIRSCREW HUB.
4 END CAP FOR IO.
5 ADJUSTING WASHER FOR END PLAY.
6 OUTER RACE OF FRONT ROLLER BEARING.
7 DISTANCE WASHER.
8 FRONT HALF OF THRUST BEARING OUTER RACE.
9 REAR HALF OF THRUST BEARING OUTER RACE.
IO THRUST HOUSING.
II AIRSCREW SHAFT GEAR WHEEL.
I2 KEEPER PLATE FOR I3.
I3 OUTER RACE OF AIRSCREW SHAFT REAR BEARING.
I4 INNER RACE OF AIRSCREW SHAFT REAR BEARING.
I5 INNER RACE OF THRUST BEARING.
I6 DISTANCE WASHER.
I7 INNER RACE OF AIRSCREW SHAFT FRONT BEARING.

I8 COUPLING SHAFT.
I9 KEEPER PLATE FOR 20.
20 OUTER RACE OF DRIVING PINION REAR BEARING.
2I DRIVING PINION.
22 HOUSING FOR 23.
23 OUTER RACE DRIVING PINION FRONT BEARING.
24 TIMING DISC.
25 OUTER RACE OF LOCATING BEARING FOR 2I.
26 BLANKING PLUG FOR TIMING WINDOW.
27 END CAP SECURING 24 TO 2I.
28 END PLATE SECURING 23 IN HOUSING.
29 INNER RACE OF LOCATING BEARING.
30 ADJUSTING WASHER FOR 30.
3I OIL FEED UNION.
32 REAR OIL JET.
33 FRONT OIL JET.

OIL JETS (PART SECTION ON A-A).

Figure 21 Rolls-Royce Kestrel reduction gear.

36

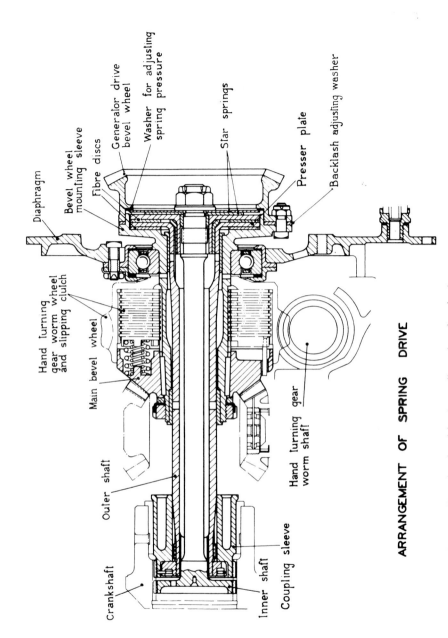

Figure 22 Rolls-Royce Kestrel spring drive (normally aspirated engines).

ARRANGEMENT OF SPRING DRIVE

Diaphragm

Bevel wheel mounting sleeve

Fibre discs

Generator drive bevel wheel

Washer for adjusting spring pressure

Star springs

Presser plate

Backlash adjusting washer

Hand turning gear worm wheel and slipping clutch

Main bevel wheel

Hand turning gear worm shaft

Outer shaft

Crankshaft

Inner shaft

Coupling sleeve

37

(1) lock positively all nuts involved in holding the bevel drive unit in position in the wheelcase and cylinder head,

(2) reduce all slacks in the drive to the minimum,

Occasional failures occurred of the bronze helical drive gearing to the magneto cross shaft and the later Merlin engine also suffered in this way. It was found that by providing sufficient backlash in the magneto drive gears, to isolate them from torsional effects, completely cured the magneto drive gear problem. This was introduced by Harvey-Bailey (By) and officially known as 'co-related backlash'.

The Company's previous practice for a spring drive (24), as used on the Eagle and Condor, was a somewhat complicated affair using a cluster of coil springs acting at a considerable radius from the crankshaft axis and the new design provided a considerable simplification and saved weight.

For starting up the engine a hand turning gear (25) was provided in the wheelcase by means of a cross shaft carrying a worm gear which could be slid into engagement with a worm wheel on the spring drive by a hand operated lever as the shaft rotated. This was a somewhat delicate operation and if done clumsily could result in the teeth of the worm wheel, which in the interests of lightness was made in aluminium, being

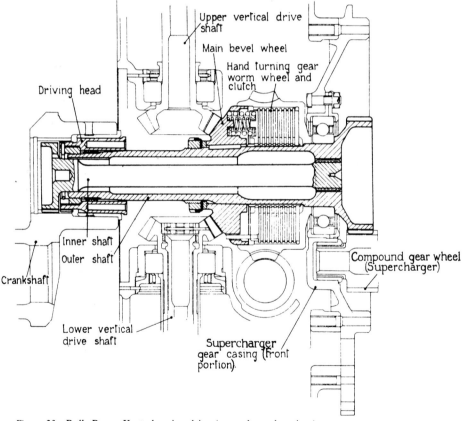

Figure 23 Rolls-Royce Kestrel spring drive (supercharged engines).

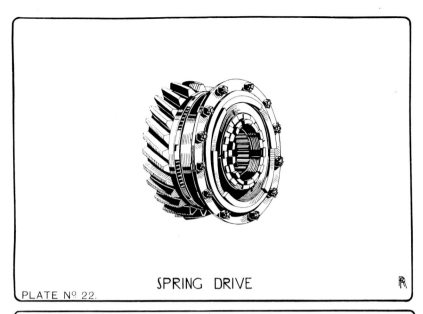

SPRING DRIVE

ℝℝ

PLATE Nº 22.

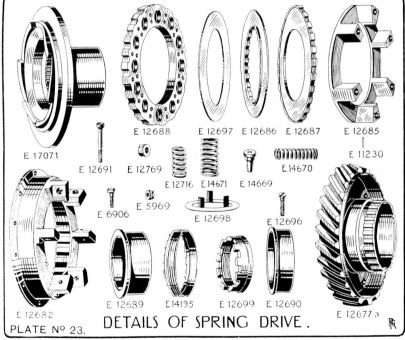

E 17071

E 12688

E 12697 E 12686 E 12687

E 12685

E 12691 E 12769

E 11230

E 14670

E 12716 E 14671 E 14669

E 6906 E 5969

E 12698

E 12696

E 12682

E 12689 E 14195 E 12699 E 12690

E 12677a

ℝℝ

PLATE Nº 23. DETAILS OF SPRING DRIVE.

Figure 24 Rolls-Royce Eagle spring drive.

badly damaged. While hand turning was proceeding the engine was primed with an appropriate volatile fuel through priming nozzles in the induction manifolds, and on firing the worm wheel would throw the worm out of engagement. An alternative form of starting was provided by a Hucks starter for which a claw was attached to the front of the propeller hub.

Later marks were provided with a compressed air starter (26) in which compressed air was supplied to non-return valves in the cylinder heads from a donkey engine consisting of a two-stroke driving a compressor, the compressed air being fed to each cylinder in turn through a distributor valve driven off the end of one camshaft. One of the problems here was apt to be starting up the two-stroke donkey engine. The system entailed the use of an inevitably untidy arrangement of small bore copper pipes between

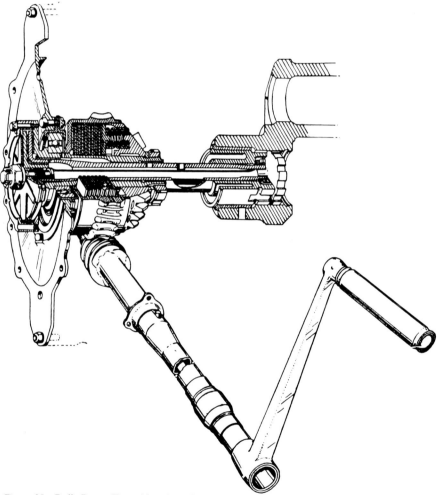

Figure 25 Rolls-Royce Kestrel hand turning gear.

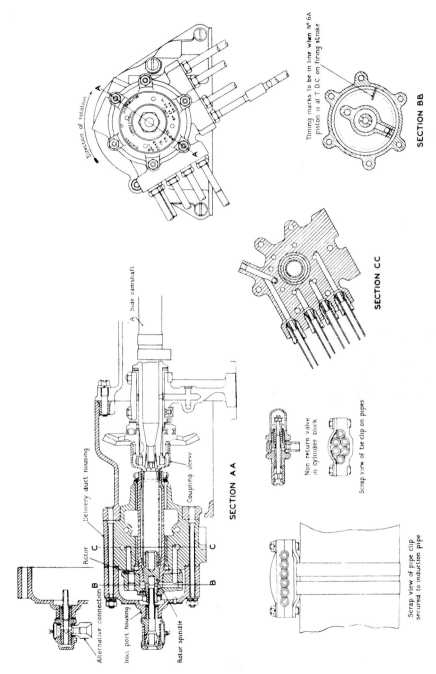

Direction of rotation

Timing marks to be in line when N° 6A
piston is at T.D.C. on firing stroke

SECTION BB

A. Side camshaft

Delivery duct housing

Coupling sleeve

SECTION AA

SECTION CC

Rotor

Alternative connection

Inlet port housing

Rotor spindle

C

B

B

C

Non return valve
in cylinder block

Scrap view of tie clip on pipes

Scrap view of pipe clip
secured to induction pipe

Figure 26 Rolls-Royce Kestrel—compressor air starter—distribution and non-return valves.

41

Figure 27 Rolls-Royce Kestrel V.

the distributor valve and the cylinder head non-return valve, which were liable to failure due to vibration. A cast-in boss had also to be provided in the cylinder head for the non-return valve and this was apt to provide an obstruction to the free flow of coolant in the head jacket in a critical area. The subsequent introduction of electric starting on later engines solved most of these problems.

A version of the non-supercharged engine was developed as an alternative to the Napier Lion for the attempted long distance nonstop flight to Capetown in a specially designed Fairey aircraft.

In order to achieve the required specific fuel consumption for this exercise, special high compression pistons were fitted to give a ratio of 8:1 instead of the normal 6:1 and a successful type test using special fuels was completed using these, and the engine held in reserve. In the event the mission was successfully achieved using the Napier Lion engine.

After the building of some naturally aspirated engines for the Hawker Hart series of aircraft, production started on the supercharged engine (**27**). To prevent over-boosting on the ground and at low altitudes it was necessary to provide an automatic boost control in the engine throttle control system (**28**). Proprietary units made by Claudel Hobson were just becoming available operated by oil pressure and using pressure sensitive capsules made by Negretti & Zambra. Royce took the view that any apparatus inserted in the throttle operating system must be absolutely reliable for obvious reasons, and he also objected to the use of engine oil pressure for the operation of such apparatus, as this introduced the possibility of loss of engine oil pressure and subsequent engine failure. He proposed instead the use of the pressure difference across the supercharger, which entailed the use of a larger servo-cylinder of some 3″ diameter. A more difficult problem was the low value of the pressure difference under idling conditions but this was solved by the use of a change-over valve which substituted the pressure difference between the supercharger inlet and ambient pressure for the pressure difference across the supercharger at an appropriate point in the throttle closing movement. He also proposed the use of:

(1) a bellows unit as used in the motor car radiator thermostat unit for operating the pressure sensing valve.

(2) the use of a small bevel gear differential unit as used in the motor car brake system to achieve the necessary control movement without the use of awkward control angles.

A successful design (29) using these proposals was evolved and developed into a reliable unit which in various different forms, and with additional items such as variable datum and a cut-out for use by the pilot in emergency, was used on all our subsequent piston engines. It was mounted on the supercharger casing so that no external connecting pipes were involved, the necessary connections being made across the mounting face. Trouble caused by wear of the ball joint between capsule and valve, due to vibration causing the latter to revolve, was cured by substituting a Hooke's coupling for the ball joint, and the original bellows were replaced by Negretti & Zambra capsules following a number of fatigue failures in service.

One advantage of the liquid-cooled engine is its ability to run for short periods at very high boost pressures because of the reserve of heat capacity in the liquid-cooled system. To take full advantage of this and to give the pilot the advantage of full operation of the throttle under emergency conditions, the cut-out referred to above was obtained by means of a valve embodied in the main casting of the unit which made the capsule and servo valve inoperative. The cut-out valve was operated from a lever in the cockpit which the pilot could move by breaking a lead seal thus indicating at the service inspection following the flight that the cut-out had been used and that certain items were therefore to be inspected before the aircraft was flown again.

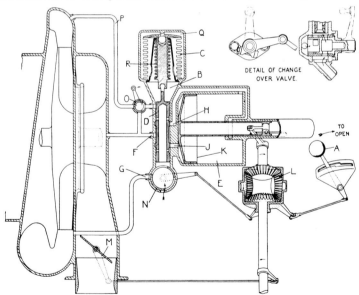

Figure 28   Rolls-Royce Kestrel—diagramatic view of automatic boost control with change-over valve (N) and cut-out valve (O).

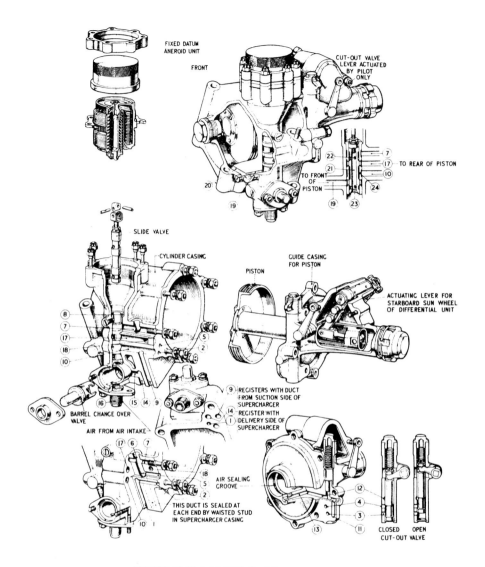

DIRECTION OF AIR FLOW THROUGH UNIT

	CONDITIONS	DIRECTION OF AIR FLOW
I	BOOST PRESSURE LESS THAN +1½LB PER SQ.INCH. CHANGE-OVER VALVE OPEN TO AIR FROM AIR INTAKE ONLY	THROUGH 9-10-24-19-20 TO FRONT OF PISTON " 16-21-22-17-18 TO REAR OF PISTON
2	BOOST PRESSURE LESS THAN +1½LB PER SQ.INCH. CHANGE-OVER VALVE OPEN TO AIR FROM DELIVERY SIDE OF BLOWER ONLY	THROUGH 9-10-24-19-20 TO FRONT OF PISTON " 14-15-21-22-17-18 TO REAR OF PISTON
3	BOOST PRESSURE MORE THAN +1½LB PER SQ.INCH. CHANGE-OVER VALVE OPEN TO AIR FROM DELIVERY SIDE OF BLOWER ONLY	THROUGH 9-10-17-18 TO REAR OF PISTON " 14-15-21-23-19-20 TO FRONT OF PISTON
4	CUT-OUT VALVE CLOSED	THROUGH 1-2-3-4-5-6-7-8 INTO ANEROID CHAMBER
5	CUT-OUT VALVE OPEN	THROUGH 9-10-11-12-4-5-6-7-8 INTO ANEROID CHAMBER

Figure 29 Rolls-Royce Kestrel—automatic boost control.

44

In the original design the supercharger rotor ran on two ball bearings but it was soon found that the rear bearing was liable to seizure due to low temperature of the aluminium casing arising from fuel evaporation, causing contraction and complete loss of running clearance. To avoid this Royce proposed a plain bearing (**30**) consisting of a number of concentric floating bushes alternatively in bronze and steel, with blind ends and spiral oil grooves to distribute oil over the running surfaces.

These bearings were very successful and it was eventually found that one pair of floating bushes was sufficient. The rotor end thrust was taken at the front by a single row deep groove ball bearing which was provided with a small radial clearance to increase its capacity for taking end thrust. End thrust was controlled by a projecting rib on the forward face of the rotor which ran in a groove in the casing with small radial clearances. The ball bearing was provided with oil flingers fore and aft to control the amount of oil passing through the bearing.

A further difficulty experienced with the supercharger arose from the effect of backfires, particularly those arising at high boost pressures from the effect of pre-ignition when quite high pressure could be generated within the casing resulting in failure of the latter and sometimes almost complete detachment of the rear portion. This problem was dealt with by providing the casing with an extra ring of bolts at the diffuser section. These bolts were shaped to conform with the diffuser vanes through which they passed, and it was necessary for them to be very accurately matched because of the high air velocities within the diffuser vanes. As boost pressures increased on later engines, it was found necessary to introduce flame traps (**31**) in the induction system to damp out back fires. This avoided the build up of pressure in the trunk pipe and supercharger and prevented the engine cutting out.

Undoubtedly the worst trouble experienced on the Kestrel in service was leaking cylinder head joints. These would sometimes lead to a cylinder becoming partially filled with water on standing, resulting in a failed connecting rod when starting up again due to trapped water. The rather puzzling feature with regard to the leaks was that they seemed to predominate on No. 3 cylinder in A block on the exhaust side and it was only after an intensive and thorough investigation by Len Hall (LBH), who at the time was assistant development engineer to Lov, that the reason for this became clear.

No. 3 cylinder liner skirt was a close fit in the crankcase bore to locate the cylinder block on the crankcase, the remaining bores being provided with clearance to allow for relative expansion between block and crankcase. In the case of No. 6 bore this clearance was in the axial direction only by making the bore slightly oval so that the block was located accurately parallel to the crankshaft on the principle of 'Hole, Slot and Pin' used extensively on scientific instruments. The effect of this was that piston side thrust from the whole block was concentrated directly on Nos 3 and 6 liners, and the direction of this was such as to tend to open the head joint on the exhaust side. Although this effect was present also on No 6 cylinders, the cylinder holding-down bolts on the end cylinders were closer in to the joint and the whole of the bolt load was also available to keep the joint closed and the combined effect of these two features was to prevent trouble there. Although similar effects were present in B block, the direction of loading due to piston side thrust was such as to tend to open the head joint on the inlet side, and the difference in temperature conditions between the inlet and exhaust sides of the head were sufficient to account for the trouble mainly occurring on A block.

The trouble was mainly overcome by a relatively small change in the design of the cylinder block. This consisted of providing additional bolts for the head joint situated

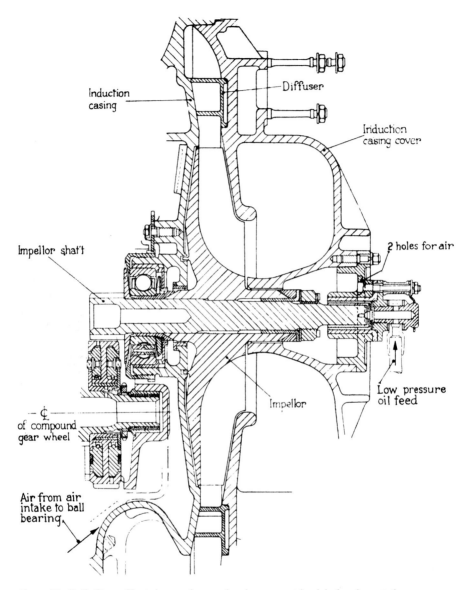

Induction casing

Diffuser

Induction casing cover

Impellor shaft

2 holes for air

Low pressure oil feed

Impellor

℄ of compound gear wheel

Air from air intake to ball bearing

Figure 30 Rolls-Royce Kestrel supercharger showing concentric plain bearings at the rear.

on the cylinder transverse axis (32). These additional bolts were inverted in the sense that they were tapped into the upper part of the cylinder head and passed through a hole drilled through a boss formed in the dividing wall in the inlet and exhaust ports and then passed into the water space beside the cylinder head joint. Each bolt was provided with a nut at its lower end which by means of a steel dog was clamped on to the underside of the liner flange, the outer end of the dog reacting against a ledge machined in the cylinder jacket wall.

In order to spanner this nut it was necessary to provide a small window in the jacket wall through which a spanner could be inserted. The window in the jacket wall was closed by means of a small cover held on with four studs. Although to apply this modification necessitated a new cylinder block casting, the changes to the casting were

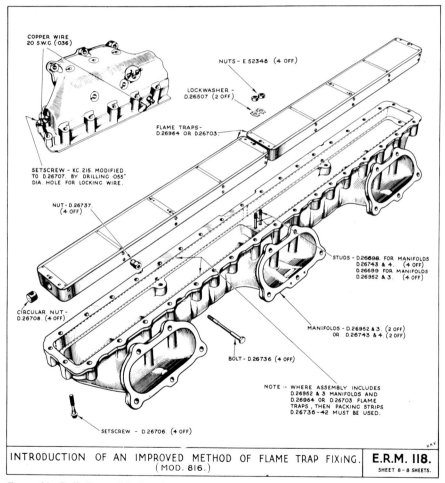

Figure 31 Rolls-Royce Merlin—flame traps of the later pattern with positive induction pipe location.

47

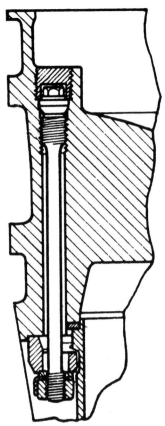

Figure 32 Cross section arrangement of liner clamp bolts to help make cylinder head joint as used on Peregrines and Merlins. (See also Figure 57).

SUPERCHARGER IMPELLOR AND SPINDLE

1. Impellor
2. Guide vane ring
3. Impellor spindle
4. Lower gear pinion
5. Higher gear pinion

6. Ball bearing assembly
7. Oil thrower, cones and locknut
8. Rear floating bushes
9. Higher gear pinion locknut

Figure 33   Rolls-Royce Merlin supercharger showing rotating inlet guide vane.

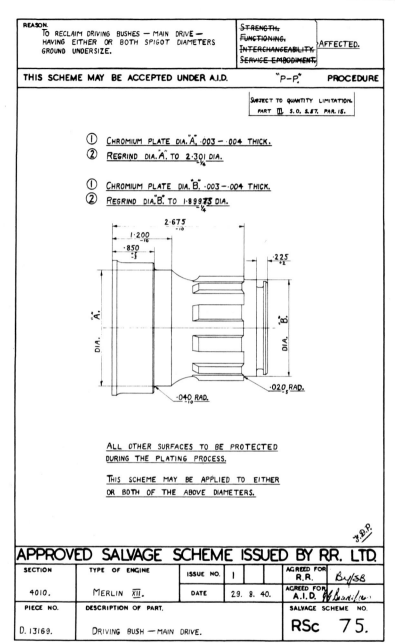

THIS SCHEME MAY BE ACCEPTED UNDER A.I.D. "P-P" PROCEDURE

SUBJECT TO QUANTITY LIMITATION.
PART III, S.O. S.57, PAR. 15.

① CHROMIUM PLATE DIA. "A". ·003 — ·004 THICK.
② REGRIND DIA. "A". TO 2·301 DIA. −¼

① CHROMIUM PLATE DIA. "B". ·003 — ·004 THICK.
② REGRIND DIA. "B". TO 1·89975 DIA. −¼

ALL OTHER SURFACES TO BE PROTECTED DURING THE PLATING PROCESS.

THIS SCHEME MAY BE APPLIED TO EITHER OR BOTH OF THE ABOVE DIAMETERS.

APPROVED SALVAGE SCHEME ISSUED BY RR. LTD.

SECTION	TYPE OF ENGINE	ISSUE NO.	I		AGREED FOR R.R.	By/SB
4010.	MERLIN XII.	DATE	29. 8. 40.		AGREED FOR A.I.D.	
PIECE NO.	DESCRIPTION OF PART.				SALVAGE SCHEME NO.	
D. 13169.	DRIVING BUSH — MAIN DRIVE.				RSc 75.	

Figure 34 Merlin salvage scheme for worn crankshaft splines.

minimal and were such that it was felt that there were not likely to be any troubles arising from these small changes. The introduction of this design in the Peregrine and Merlin provided a considerable improvement with regard to the incidence of cylinder top joint leaks. Eventually this trouble was cured by the adoption of the two-piece cylinder block with a 'dry' top joint on the Merlin.

A further development in the supercharger section was a different form of entry into the supercharger impeller which gave direct axial flow instead of the former swirl in the direction of rotation, and in conjunction with this it was necessary to provide rotating inlet guide vanes at the impeller eye (33). These guide vanes were bent at an angle to reduce shock to the entering air and by their use provided an increase in pressure rise through the impeller.

One service trouble which appeared after a fairly lengthy running period was wear of the internal castellations in the bore of the 7th journal of the crankshaft which drove the spring drive, and it was necessary to evolve a salvage scheme to avoid the scrapping of an expensive piece. The salvage scheme (34) consisted of an adaptor piece which carried the castellations at a larger radius and was made in hardenable material. This was inserted into the crankshaft (35) in a press fit and driven through the original worn castellations which were cleaned up to a new dimension. This was so successful in clearing the original trouble that the use of a similar arrangement was carried on for later engine types, although the later ones of hardenable crankshaft material might have made such a scheme less necessary.

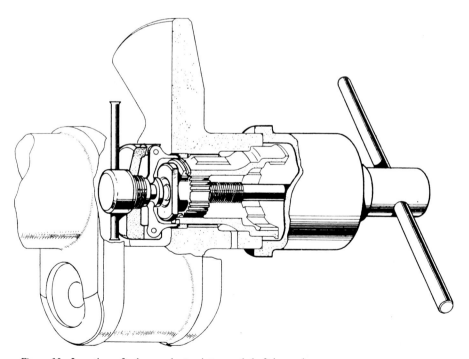

Figure 35　Insertion of salvage adaptor into crankshaft journal.

51

THE GOSHAWK AND PEREGRINE

A later development of the Kestrel which was covered by the change in name to Goshawk (**36**) introduced evaporative cooling as a means of reducing drag by virtue of reduced radiator areas resulting from this. The Goshawk was ordered in small quantities to power various experimental fighters[5] (**37,38,39 & 40**). With this system (**41**) the coolant in the jackets was allowed to boil, the resultant mixture of water and steam being separated out in the header tank and the water returning to the inlet side of the circulating pump, the condensed water being returned into the circuit by means of a displacement pump of the gear type driven off the lower end of the impeller shaft of the main circulating pump. The hot-well pump introduced many problems with regard to wear of the pump and casings, and this led to the introduction of carbon bushes for the former and end plates in a similar material for the latter. It was mainly difficulties of this sort that led to the abandonment of this type of cooling system. It was replaced by 100% Ethylene Glycol as a cooling medium, and subsequently by pressure water cooling, using Glycol as an anti-freeze. Both achieved the objective of reduction of radiator size by virtue of the increased coolant temperatures these systems allowed.

[5] Late in 1931 following the unparalleled success of the water cooled Kestrels in front line aircraft, the Air Ministry issued their specification F7/30 for a single seat day and night interceptor fighter powered by its evaporatively cooled development, the Goshawk (or Kestrel IV). Several tenders were received, and the Air Ministry selected the Supermarione Type 224, Westland PV4 and Blackburn F3 to proceed to the prototype stage, leaving Bristol and Hawker to proceed with their designs (Type 123 and PV3 respectively) as private ventures. The Goshawk also powered the unique and tailless Westland Pterodactyl MK V.

Figure 36   Rolls-Royce Goshawk fitted with ramp head blocks.

At about this time, also, design and development work was started on the replacement of parts of the water pump which were subject to considerable wear; the screw-down type of stuffing box gland, the grease lubricated plain white metal impeller spindle bearings and the footstep bearing in lignum-vitae material. Instead we used two ball bearings and a bellows mounted shoulder rotating against a fixed carbon block. These features were to appear on later Merlins when satisfactory designs had evolved (**42**).

This period also saw the development by J Ellor (Lr) of a new type of carburettor air intake in which an increase in pressure was obtained by making use of a diverging duct, the size of entry to which was matched to the aircraft speed and a similar treatment was applied to radiator cowls in the interest of reducing drag.

A further development of the Kestrel occurred in connection with a twin-engined fighter - the Westland Whirlwind (**43**). This involved the use of opposite revolving propellers to improve aircraft handling, particularly during the take-off phase and also the use of a downdraught carburettor to enable the use of an air intake positioned in the V between the cylinder blocks, in the interest of further reductions in drag. For this installation it was decided to hand all the engine components necessary to provide reverse rotation. This was a considerable complication and was abandoned on future engines. This experience led to the use of a special reduction gear for the Merlin engines used in the de Havilland Hornet aircraft in which an idler gear was introduced to obtain reverse rotation of the propeller, leaving other engine components unaltered. The Kestrel development for the Whirlwind was named Peregrine (**44**), and this aircraft/engine combination saw service at the time of the Battle of Britain and for a period afterwards.

Figure 37   The Supermarine type 224 prototype K2890—Predecessor to the Spitfire.

53

Figure 38 The Westland PV 4 prototype K2891.

Figure 39 The Blackburn F3 prototype K2892—Taxying trials were plagued by engine cooling and other problems. The Air Ministry withdrew its support and the aircraft never flew.

Figure 40 The Westland Pterodactyl V.

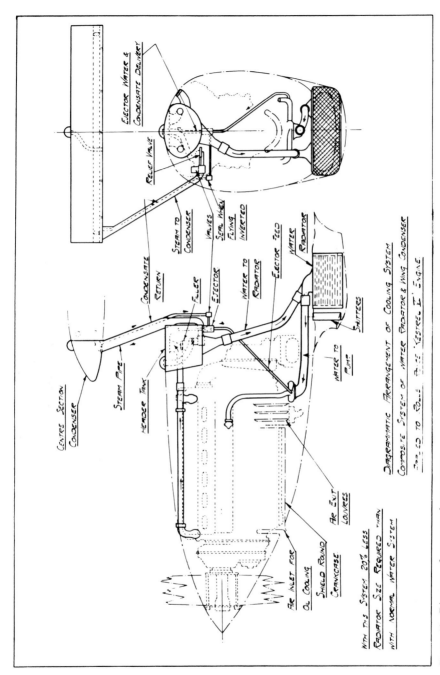

Figure 41 Diagram of steam coolant systems.

56

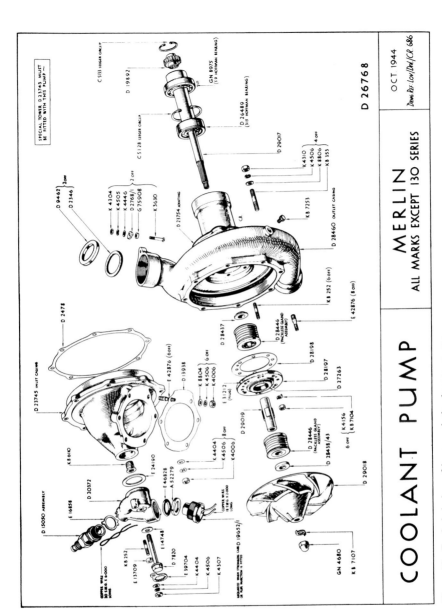

Figure 42 Exploded view of improved gland water pump.

Figure 43 The Westland Whirlwind powered by two Rolls-Royce Peregrines.

Figure 44 Rolls-Royce Peregrine—showing the downdraught carburettor installation.

THE BUZZARD AND THE 'R' ENGINE

While development of the Kestrel was proceeding it was decided to design a scaled-up version called the 'H' originally, this eventually becoming known as the Buzzard (**45**). The scale-up ratio was as 5:6, the application being in large flying boats. The engine was designed to be moderately supercharged from the beginning and was so equipped, this type of supercharging being most suitable for the flying boat application which demands high power for take-off. During the design, opportunity was taken to spread the cylinder centres a little bit further and an additional pair of cylinder holding-down studs intermediate between the main bearing panels were introduced. Those in the main bearing panels could thus be moved somewhat closer together to give a more even spacing on the cylinder head joint loading. This arrangement proved to be completely free of the trouble that had dogged the Kestrel in this area and also proved to be satisfactory under very high boost pressures as obtained on the racing version known as the 'R' used in the Schneider Cup races of 1929 and 1931. These additional cylinder holding-down studs were known as saddle studs (**46**) and to avoid stress concentration in the V in the crankcase were provided with a T shaped foot held down to the crankcase by two smaller studs. This constructional feature proved quite successful and gave no trouble.

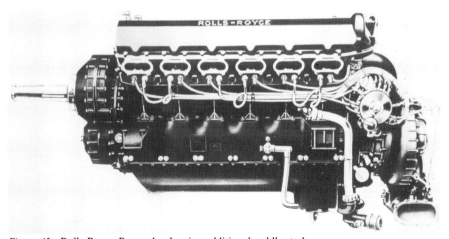

Figure 45   Rolls-Royce Buzzard—showing additional saddle studs.

Figure 46   Saddle studs.

59

Figure 47 Rolls-Royce 'R' engine (1929 model) showing double sided supercharger.

For the 'R' engine (**47**) a special supercharger was designed having a double entry eye in order to provide sufficient entry area into both sides of the impeller for the increased mass flows required and also a divergent intake in the 'V' in the interests of reduced drag.

A further novel feature on this engine was that the rocker covers were left exposed to the slipstream in order to provide additional oil cooling. This required the provision of machined faces to provide attachment for the engine cowling, and the propeller reduction gear was also provided with an extended nose to suit the aircraft cowling lines.

Running at high boost pressures revealed a weakness in the connecting rods in the arched feet of the forked rod (**48**) which were subject to bending loads. This weakness was discovered rather late in the day in the programme leading up to the race, and the forked rod feet were strengthened by widening them at the expense of making the blade rod slightly narrower. This proved to be satisfactory in the 1929 race, but to allow for further power development a design of articulated connecting rod was produced and used for the 1931 race (**49**). Balance weights were also introduced on the crankshaft in the interests of reducing main bearing loads due to inertia effects.

A similar articulated rod was also designed and used for the Goshawk version of the Kestrel engine which had been produced for application to a day and night fighter aircraft. The use of articulated connecting rods was regarded as somewhat of a nuisance because it inevitably gave a longer stroke on the articulated rod side. This led to difficulties with regard to the position of the bottom scraper ring on pistons, which required a lengthened liner skirt to prevent run-out of the ring, and in turn tended to require the raising of the cylinder block mounting platform on the crankcase and giving rise to increased frontal areas. To get over these difficulties by reverting to the forked rod construction, A J Rowledge (Rg) proposed a modification of the forked rod which provided an arch shaped foot between the forked rod and the big end bearing block itself.

This lead to the rather novel feature that the joint so formed was no longer normal to the bolt axis in the transverse plane (**50**). This in practice produced no difficulties by the virtue of fact that the bolt shanks were fitting in the bolt holes and therefore

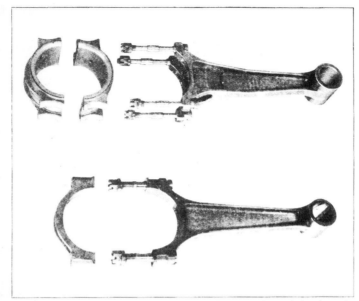

Figure 48 Rolls-Royce Kestrel—fork and blade connecting rods for the early
marks with initial type of arched foot with surface normal to bolt
axis—similar to that initially used on the Buzzard and 'R' engines.

Figure 49 Connecting rod assemblies
Top left: Kestrel—forked with lead-bronze bearings
Bottom left: Kestrel—forked with whitemetal bearing
Centre: Goshawk—articulated with lead-bronze bearing
Top right: 'R' engine—articulated with whitemetal bearings—1931 Trophy
Bottom right: 'R' engine—forked with whitemetal bearings—1929 Trophy.

61

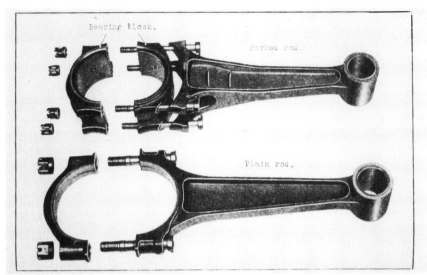

Figure 50 Rolls-Royce Kestrel—fork and blade connecting rods for the later marks with the curved foot no longer normal to the bolt axis.

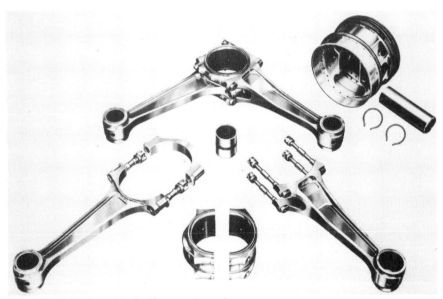

Figure 51 Rolls-Royce Merlin II connecting rods.

prevented any tendency to spread the forked rod feet under compressive loading. This type of construction therefore became standard on all future engine types (**51**).

One of the difficulties experienced with the forked connecting rod construction was the fact that the big end bearing block attached to the forked rod required to be faced with lead-bronze material on both the inner diameter and on the outer track provided for the blade rod. This was a difficult production job and prevented the use of the most suitable lead-bronze mixes for the two bearing applications. A big end design was therefore put in hand introducing thin detachable bearing shells for these applications, this requiring slight adjustment of the big end bolt centres to allow for the thickness of the separate shells. Location of the shells rotationally was prevented by a pressed-out tang on the shell split line which required a local clearance slot to be milled in the rod big end to accommodate this feature. This modified design was found to work very satisfactorily and proved to be a great easement on production as it enabled the bearing shells themselves to be obtained from specialist suppliers in this field, and also allowed the use of lead-bronze types most suited to the two differing bearing applications. This change applied to both the later Kestrels and the Merlin. It also enabled easy replacement of damaged bearing shells and facilitated engine repair work.

THE MERLIN

In the early 1930s it became evident that a larger engine than the Kestrel would be required. It was called PV12 with a bore and stroke of 5.4 x 6 in, initially giving around 750 hp. It was developed into the 1000 hp Merlin (**52**). In order to provide a more rigid engine carcase, to allow for higher crankshaft speeds, it was decided to cast the cylinder jacket portion of the cylinder block in one piece with the crankcase and to provide a separate cylinder head with the cylinder liner joint flange clamped between it and the crankcase. This presented quite a foundry problem in maintaining sectional thickness throughout, but this was solved in due course. It was soon discovered, however, on development that a major difficulty was presented because failures in the reciprocating components usually resulted in serious damage to the large crankcase-cum-cylinder jacket casting, this proving an expensive replacement and time-consuming job. Moreover, it was considered that once the separate jacket was bolted to the crankcase the final result, as regards the rigidity of the assembly, was very little different from the one-piece casting and the weight saving achieved by the latter was also small, so the principle of the one-piece crankcase and jacket was abandoned and never raised again. It was, however, used successfully on the V12 engine (**53**) of the Phantom III motor car.

The ramp cylinder head

At about this time considerable single-cylinder development work had been done on different forms of cylinder head with the objective of providing improved turbulence and thus delaying the onset of detonation and, finally, pre-ignition. The most successful of the various types tested was found to be what came to be known as the ramp head

Figure 52   Rolls-Royce Merlin III.

64

Figure 53 Rolls-Royce Phantom III V12 engine—7340 cc—note one piece cylinder block and crankcase.

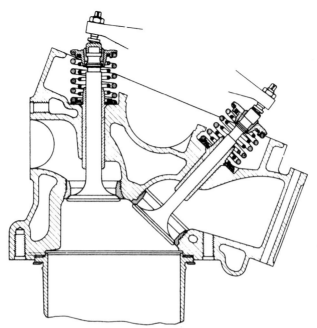

Figure 54   Rolls-Royce Merlin I—cross section of the ramp head.

(54). In this the exhaust valves remained parallel to the cylinder axis but the portion of the head carrying the inlet valves was inclined to give an easier flow into the head. The shape of the head, viewed from underneath, was roughly square, the side dimension of the square being considerably less than the cylinder bore diameter and thus providing considerable 'squish' turbulence from the piston at the top of its stroke. Apart from the turbulence effect, this head was also found to give a considerable improvement in power relative to boost pressure on a single-cylinder unit. On the basis of these results it was decided to proceed with the design of this engine using a ramp type head. In order to obtain more experience of this type of head it was also decided to design a version to suit the Goshawk engine known as Goshawk B, and considerable satisfactory running experience was quickly obtained on an engine so converted.

The valve gear to suit this type of head inevitably had to be different from the type of head using parallel inlet and exhaust valves and was of the type using a central camshaft operating rocker arms above it, which gave reversal of operation to the valves themselves **(55)**. This type of head also demanded the head to be separate from the cylinder jacket and this led to a construction in which the top flange of the liner was clamped between the top deck of the jacket and the bottom deck of the head. When cylinder blocks of this type were tried on the Merlin it was found that the increase in power relative to boost pressure obtained on the single cylinder unit was not achieved on the main engine and, although considerable investigation was put in hand to find out why this should be so, this point was never solved and it was concluded that this effect was peculiar to the single cylinder unit. The improvement in detonation characteristics was not felt on the engine, being worse than with the normal head, and

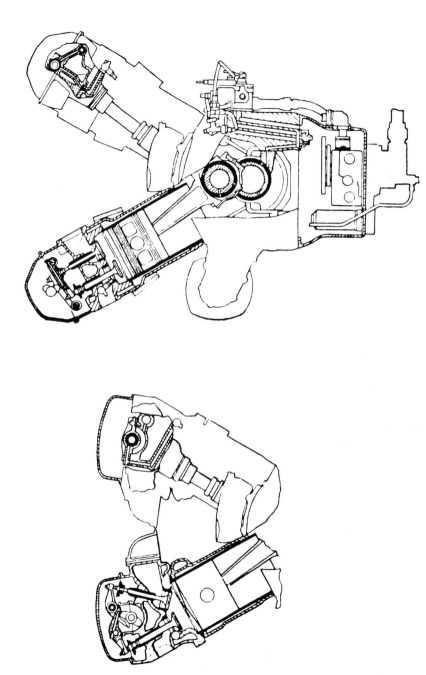

Figure 55 Comparison of the Merlin I ramp head (on the left) with that of the Merlin II flat head (on the right).

a further trouble presented itself on the type test when a hole was burned through the exhaust port wall into the coolant jacket space causing a spectacular fire of the glycol coolant. This had occurred several times previously and the reason for it was never fully explained but was considered to be due to local overheating due to pre-ignition and late burning of the charge. A further serious trouble was wear and break-up of the rocker pads due to the effect of friction between cam and pad increasing the unit loading between the operating surfaces. To deal with this latter trouble the geometry of the valve gear was modified to reduce this friction effect which resulted in asymmetric shaped cams and, although improving conditions somewhat, was never considered to be as satisfactory as the valve gear used in conjunction with parallel valves on the engine with normal flat head cylinders.

Due to the urgent requirement for these engines for the Fairey Battle aircraft and in view of the situation which was developing with regard to war with Germany, it was decided to order 172 Merlin I engines (**56**) having this type of cylinder block although a satisfactory full type test was never completed due to the port burning referred to above, and a decision was made to revert to the one-piece cylinder block with flat head (**57**) which had been satisfactorily developed on the Kestrel.

Although a design for a two-piece cylinder block with a flat head had been worked out, it was considered that more experience would be required with this before putting into quantity production as it was felt that the bottom deck of the separate cylinder head might adversely affect the cooling of the head, particularly in the region of the sparking plug bosses.

The single piece block was provided from the start with liner clamp bolts, which worked well until increasing boost pressures and power development forced the introduction of the two-piece block

Figure 56   Rolls-Royce Merlin I showing the ramp head.

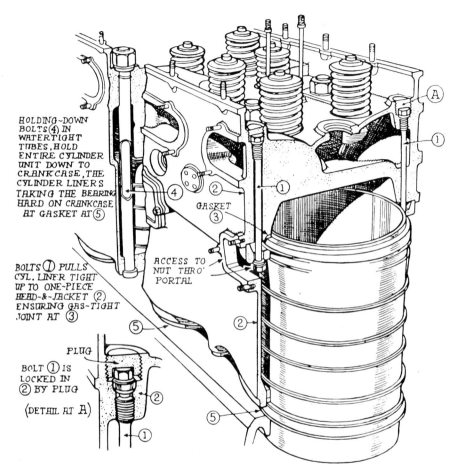

HOLDING-DOWN BOLTS(4) IN WATERTIGHT TUBES, HOLD ENTIRE CYLINDER UNIT DOWN TO CRANKCASE, THE CYLINDER LINERS TAKING THE BEARING HARD ON CRANKCASE AT GASKET AT(5)

GASKET
(3)

ACCESS TO NUT THRO' PORTAL

BOLTS(1) PULLS CYL. LINER TIGHT UP TO ONE-PIECE HEAD-&-JACKET (2) ENSURING GAS-TIGHT JOINT AT (3)

PLUG

BOLT(1) IS LOCKED IN (2) BY PLUG

(DETAIL AT A)

Figure 57 Rolls-Royce Merlin—One piece cylinder block showing flat head and liner clamp bolts.

69

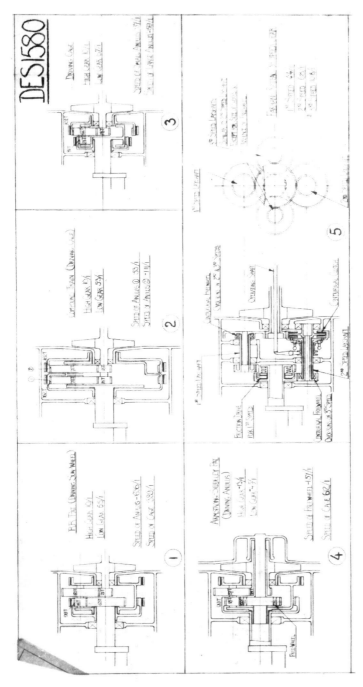

Figure 58 An early project design scheme showing various multiple speed drives—No. 3 being the type initially used whilst No. 5 represents the more conventional type of Farman drive finally used.

Supercharger and auxiliary drives

The next major feature introduced on the Merlin was a two-speed drive for the supercharger so as to combine the advantages of moderate supercharging and high altitude supercharging on the one engine type. Some preliminary work (**58**)[6] had already been done on this feature on the Kestrel and great efforts were made to provide a gear that could be accommodated within the existing engine length measurements. A design was finally achieved (**59**) which only lengthened the engine by $\frac{1}{2}''$ so as to provide as little difficulty as possible with regard to aircraft installation.

A form of epicyclic gear was adopted in which the cage was driven from the crankshaft through the normal spring drive and provided with duplex planet gears meshing with appropriate duplex sun gears and also corresponding internally toothed annulus gears, one of which could be locked against rotation by means of a plate clutch and the other by means of a freewheel of the jamming roller type. The clutch was spring loaded, the pressure plate of which could be released by revolving this against a circle of inclined short pillars with hemispherical ends. The type of freewheel (**60**) we selected to use was known as the Humphrey-Sandberg using rollers that were constrained to lie inclined to the axis of rotation and this proved to be our undoing as we were never able to get this to run in the freewheel regime without unacceptable overheating and this turned out to be the general experience with this type of freewheel in other applications (**61,62**)[7].

At about this time a more conventional design of two-speed supercharger drive (**63,64**) had been brought out by the Farman Company in Paris. This used a fixed layshaft arrangement using two layshafts oppositely positioned for the high altitude ratio and a single layshaft for the moderate ratio, this giving a balanced drive for the former to ensure minimum bearing loads on the supercharger rotor shaft at the highest speeds.

The three layshafts were provided with plate clutches operated by centrifugal bobweights which could be released through the medium of ball thrust bearings. I went to Paris to visit the Farman Company to obtain their proposals and although the adoption of this type of gear meant increasing the engine length by some 3 in, it was decided to proceed in view of the difficulties which we had met on the Kestrel, and a licence was negotiated with the Farman Company.

In our case the operation of the clutches (**65**) was obtained through the medium of a camshaft which was operated by engine scavenge oil pressure following the system as described for the two-speed propeller reduction gear designed for the Eagle engine.

In order to deal with the service troubles which had occurred on the Kestrel engine in the camshaft drives, a modified wheelcase design (**66**) was introduced in which the nest of three bevels transmitting the drive to the inclined shafts to the cylinder heads could be exposed to view by the removal of a simple cover over the top of the wheelcase. This enabled the very close meshing of these bevels to be obtained by visual inspection, as found necessary to eliminate as far as possible any backlash in the camshaft drive because of the frequent torque reversal which occurs during a revolution of the camshaft. This design also made it possible to make the inclined bevels in one piece with their shafts and so avoided a fixing which in time could work loose.

A further feature arising from the need for extra drives (**67**) for aircraft auxiliaries was provided by a very simple arrangement of a gear mounted on bearings on the ends

---

[6] Actually drawn by Rbr in November 1931 and initialled AAR.
[7] A similar type of freewheel was used in the hand starter gear of the Merlin II but following starting problems was deleted on the Merlin III.

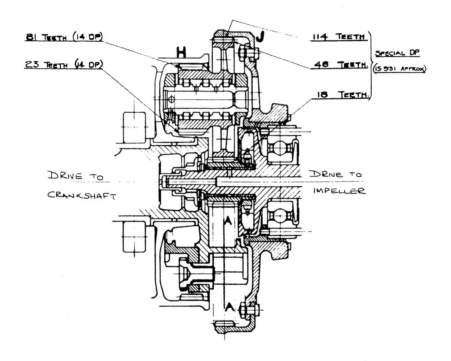

J FIXED - RATIO = 7.333 : 1 (MODERATE S/C).

H FIXED - RATIO = 10.39 : 1 (FULL S/C).

81 TEETH (14 DP)

23 TEETH (14 DP)

H

J

114 TEETH

48 TEETH.

18 TEETH.

SPECIAL DP.
(15.931 APPROX)

DRIVE TO
CRANKSHAFT

DRIVE TO
IMPELLER

GOSHAWK.
2-SPEED SUPERCHARGER.
(REVISED RATIOS).

11. 7. 34

Figure 59   Rolls-Royce Goshawk epicyclic two-speed supercharger drive.

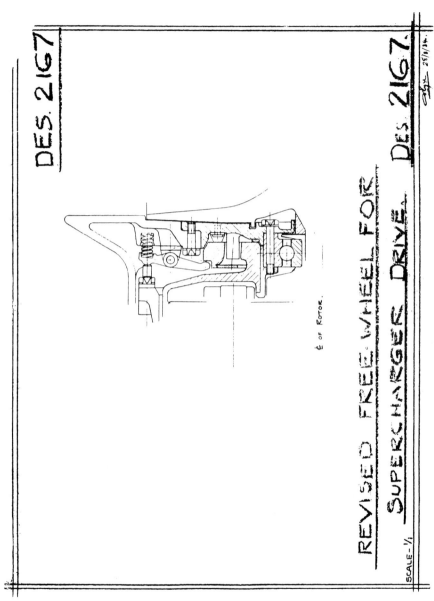

Figure 60 Rolls-Royce Goshawk—inclined roller freewheel on the epicyclic supercharger drive—similar operation to that used on the Merlin II hand starter gear.

73

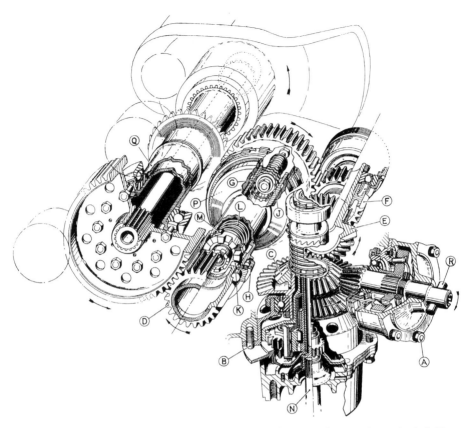

Figure 61 Rolls–Royce Merlin II—starter system gear drive—electric motor input via shaft N—hand starter drive via shaft R including the inclined roller freewheel.

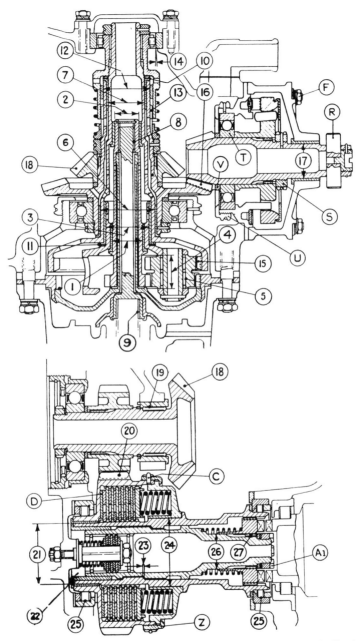

Figure 62 Cross section of Merlin II starter system gear drive—note inclined roller freewheel on the upper right.

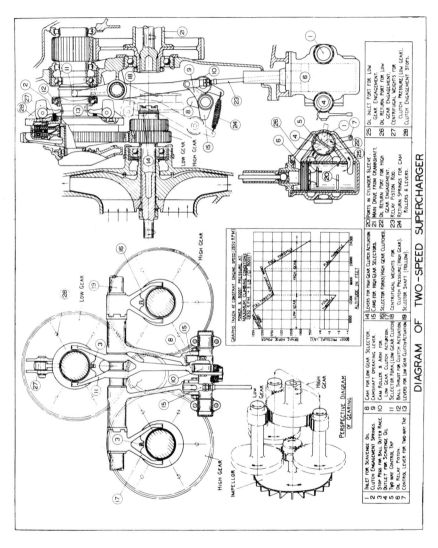

Figure 63 Rolls-Royce Merlin XX series—two-speed supercharger drive—Farman type.

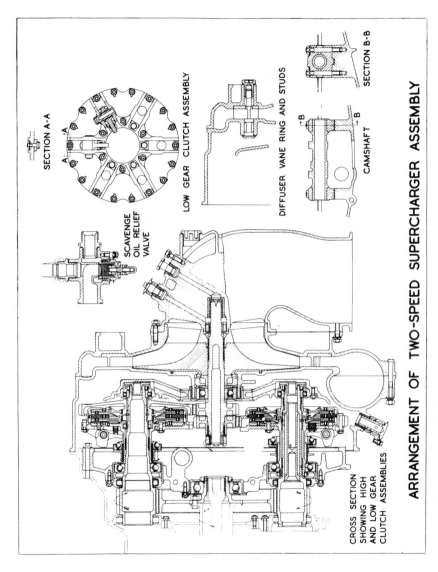

SECTION A-A

LOW GEAR CLUTCH ASSEMBLY

DIFFUSER VANE RING AND STUDS

SECTION B-B

CAMSHAFT

SCAVENGE
OIL RELIEF
VALVE

CROSS SECTION
SHOWING HIGH
AND LOW GEAR
CLUTCH ASSEMBLIES

ARRANGEMENT OF TWO-SPEED SUPERCHARGER ASSEMBLY

Figure 64 Rolls-Royce Merlin XX series—two-speed supercharger drive—Farman type.

77

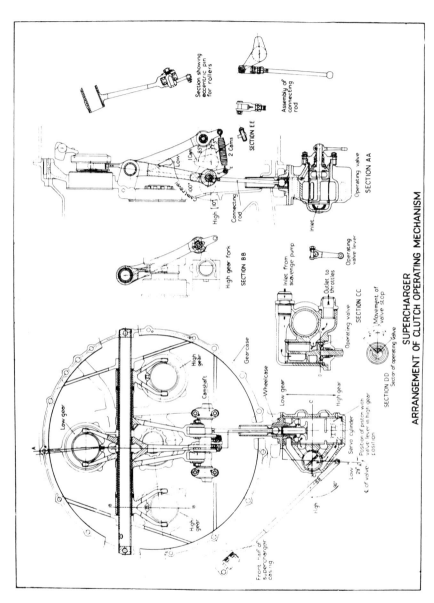

Figure 65   Rolls-Royce Merlin—two-speed supercharger clutch operating mechanism.

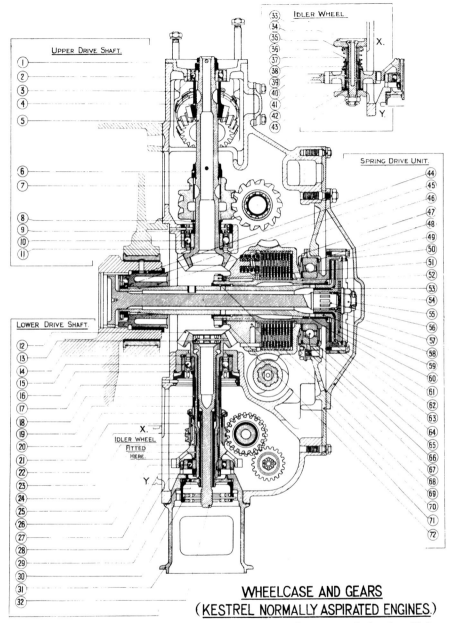

UPPER DRIVE SHAFT.

① ② ③ ④ ⑤ ⑥ ⑦ ⑧ ⑨ ⑩ ⑪

LOWER DRIVE SHAFT.

⑫ ⑬ ⑭ ⑮ ⑯ ⑰ ⑱ ⑲ ⑳ ㉑ ㉒ ㉓ ㉔ ㉕ ㉖ ㉗ ㉘ ㉙ ㉚ ㉛ ㉜

IDLER WHEEL

㉝ ㉞ ㉟ ㊱ ㊲ ㊳ ㊴ ㊵ ㊶ ㊷ ㊸

X.

Y.

SPRING DRIVE UNIT.

㊹ ㊺ ㊻ ㊼ ㊽ ㊾ ㊿ 51 52 53 54 55 56 57 58 59 60 61 62 63 64 65 66 67 68 69 70 71 72

X.
IDLER WHEEL
FITTED
HERE.

Y.

WHEELCASE AND GEARS
(KESTREL NORMALLY ASPIRATED ENGINES.)

Figure 66 Rolls-Royce Kestrel wheelcase showing the cover to give access to the bevels and below the cover the skew gear drive to the magnetos.

79

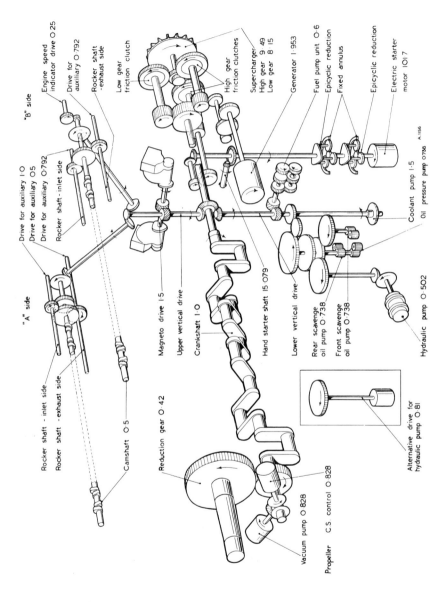

"B" side

Engine speed indicator drive O·25
Drive for auxiliary O·792
Rocker shaft -exhaust side
Low gear friction clutch

High gear friction clutches
Supercharger—
High gear 9·49
Low gear 8·15
Generator 1·953
Fuel pump unit O·6
Epicyclic reduction
Fixed annulus
Epicyclic reduction
Electric starter motor 1O·17

A·1156

Coolant pump 1·5
Oil pressure pump O·738

"A" side

Drive for auxiliary 1·O
Drive for auxiliary O·5
Drive for auxiliary O·792
Rocker shaft -inlet side

Rocker shaft - inlet side
Rocker shaft - exhaust side

Camshaft O·5

Reduction gear O·42

Magneto drive 1·5
Upper vertical drive
Crankshaft 1·O

Hand starter shaft 15·O79

Lower vertical drive

Rear scavenge oil pump O·738
Front scavenge oil pump O·738

Hydraulic pump O·5O2

Alternative drive for hydraulic pump O·81

Vacuum pump O·828

Propeller   C.S. control O·828

Figure 67   Rolls-Royce Merlin XX series geartrain showing auxiliary drives.

80

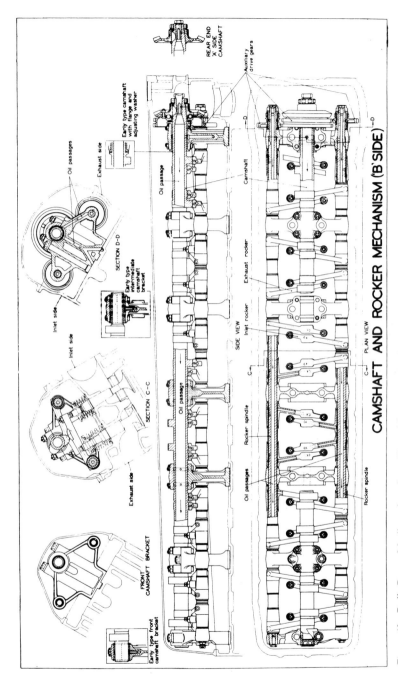

Figure 68 Rolls-Royce Merlin—aircraft auxiliary drives on ends of rockershafts.

of the rocker shafts which drove the auxiliary through splines and a quill shaft (**68**). In order to provide a mounting face for the actual auxiliary unit it was necessary to raise the height of the cylinder head rocker cover face joint at the back end where these auxiliaries were to be mounted and, in order to avoid difficulties with removal of the rocker shafts in situ should this be required in service, the level of the rocker cover joint face had to be left in its original position at the front end, this involving a sloping joint face at the top of the cylinder block. The latter was not liked as a production feature but was accepted as inevitable and, once the proper equipment had been provided for producing it, no serious troubles were experienced on production.

These drives proved to be rather rough because of the torque reversal effect in the camshaft referred to above, this resulting in failure of the quill shaft driving the auxiliary unit. To deal with this problem an attempt was made to provide some flexibility in the drive to the auxiliary unit by a design based on a magneto drive originally used on cars. This consisted of a pack of plate springs clamped diametrically between jaws machined in the end of the quill shaft, such an arrangement giving some damping in addition to increased flexibility. Such drives, however, were not immune from occasional failure of the spring plates themselves, and the most satisfactory solution to this trouble was achieved by the use of a bonded rubber coupling. This was applied to one unit only, normal quill shafts being used on most auxiliaries (**69**).

This general arrangement provided an additional four drives at the back end of the engine and use was made eventually of all of these in the various aircraft installations until the introduction of a separately mounted auxiliary gearbox driven by a single shaft off the supercharger drive referred to later on. Two further auxiliary drives were provided by a cluster of bevel gears carried in a small casting mounted on the front end of the reduction gear casing on the crankshaft centreline and driven off the reduction gear pinion (**70**). These two drives were specifically for the constant speed unit for the propeller and a vacuum pump provided for aircraft instruments, and it was necessary to cant the axes of these units so that in the front view they came within the circle of the propeller spinner. A further important drive (**71**) for an electric generator for aircraft services was provided at the side of the crankcase, the generator itself being mounted on a part circular facing formed on the crankcase wall and held down to it by means of steel straps. The drive to this was taken from a train of gears driven from the main spring drive, the final drive shaft to the generator armature being carried in bearings within the engine rear mounting foot.

In the early days of the two-speed supercharger drive some trouble was experienced with regard to the setting up of the withdrawal mechanism for the layshaft plate clutches and a procedure for this had to be adopted to a schedule drawn up by the Design Office. The sequence was followed in all factories and much improved the situation. The drive was further improved by the use of ground solid steel clutch plates in place of the built up and riveted units first used. Some trouble was also experienced with failures of the moderate supercharger layshaft gear, due to fatigue cracks in the rim. The gear was of the umbrella type with overhung teeth. It was eventually found that the gear failed in a bell mode of vibration, excited by tooth contacts. It was cured by modifying the clutch pack, so that the gear could have its web centrally disposed to the teeth.

Two-piece cylinder block

With extended service hours and the use of higher boost pressures various troubles began to appear in the region of the cylinder heads; one of these was leaking of the

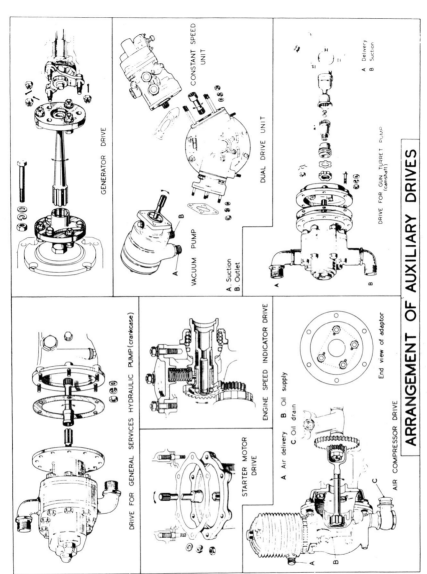

GENERATOR DRIVE

CONSTANT SPEED UNIT

DUAL DRIVE UNIT

VACUUM PUMP

A. Suction
B. Outlet

DRIVE FOR GUN TURRET PUMP (camshaft)

A Delivery
B Suction

DRIVE FOR GENERAL SERVICES HYDRAULIC PUMP (crankcase)

ENGINE SPEED INDICATOR DRIVE

STARTER MOTOR DRIVE

End view of adaptor

A Air delivery   B Oil supply
C Oil drain

AIR COMPRESSOR DRIVE

ARRANGEMENT OF AUXILIARY DRIVES

Figure 69   Rolls-Royce Merlin—auxiliary drives.

83

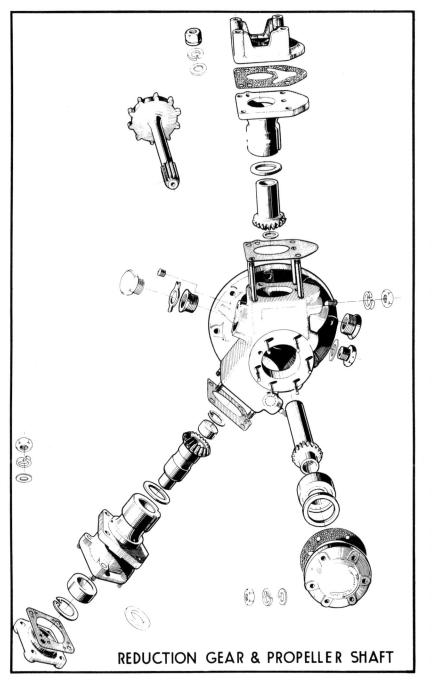

REDUCTION GEAR & PROPELLER SHAFT

Figure 70   Rolls-Royce Merlin—auxiliary drives from propellor reduction gear known as the dual drive unit.

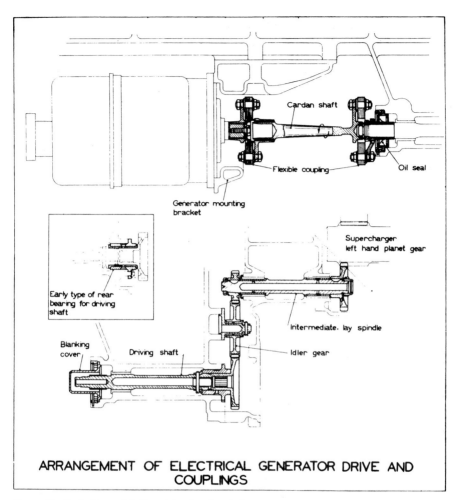

Cardan shaft

Flexible coupling

Oil seal

Generator mounting bracket

Supercharger left hand planet gear

Early type of rear bearing for driving shaft

Intermediate. lay spindle

Blanking cover

Driving shaft

Idler gear

ARRANGEMENT OF ELECTRICAL GENERATOR DRIVE AND COUPLINGS

Figure 71 Rolls-Royce Merlin—drive for electrical generator.

liner-head joint and to deal with this a reversion was proposed to the two-piece construction of separate head and jackets but retaining, of course, the flat head (**72**).

In the meantime various attempts to improve the single-piece block were made, the most effective being to saw-cut through the material joining adjacent cylinder heads which it was found could easily be done by the use of a fine circular saw carried on a fixture inserted through the lower end of the cylinder jackets. The purpose of this was to provide additional flexibility to allow for any slight discrepancies in the lengths between flanges of adjacent liners and also, incidentally, to give improved cooling to the head by virtue of the coolant present in the gap so formed. This was found to give some improvement in service but insufficient to cause us to abandon the two-piece construction for later Merlins as mentioned previously.

A further change was also tried in which the intermediate main holding-down studs were shortened so that their nuts and clamps could seat directly on to bosses formed on the cylinder heads within the coolant space instead of the load being applied from the top deck. These nuts had to be spannered through holes in the top deck which were subsequently plugged by removable plugs. Such an arrangement gave a more highly localised loading at the joint, as indeed might have been expected compared with loading from the top deck through the port side walls, and it gave no improvement and was therefore abandoned.

In the two-piece construction the top flange of the liner is clamped between the head and jacket giving a dry joint as far as leakage of coolant into the cylinder was concerned, and cross connections have to be made between the jacket and head to provide the necessary coolant flow. These were made by bobbins which made a seal with bores provided for them in the head and jacket by means of circular section rubber rings carried in grooves in the bobbins (**73**). The making of the joint between liner, head and jacket was further reinforced by additional studs, two on each side, carried in tappings in the cylinder head below the valve ports and engaging corresponding deep bosses formed on the jacket side walls. This arrangement of a pair of studs instead of a single stud on the cylinder centreline enabled the width across the port faces of the cylinder head to be retained at the original dimension, thus avoiding changes to the inlet manifolding. This construction also had the benefit of additional beam stiffness by virtue of the presence of the additional longitudinal walls at the base of the cylinder head and at the top of the jacket portion, thus adding to the general beam stiffness of the engine carcase to deal with explosion and rotating loads.

Another persistent trouble in the cylinder head was cracking of the rather thin bar of material between the pairs of valve ports. This caused no trouble when the cracks ran between inlet ports and was acceptable at repair. There was not much that could be done dimensionally to improve the situation because of the restriction on the inner diameter of the cylinder head, and a considerable improvement was eventually achieved by improving the properties of the material in this area of the head by means of the use of local chills during the casting process. Some trouble was also experienced with cracking of the cylinder liner immediately underneath the top flange and this was considered to be due to the deflection of the liner under the effects of piston side thrust, and the cure for this was to provide increased local thickness by means of a taper and a transition radius (**74**).

Troubles were also experienced with coolant leakage from the lower joint between liner and jacket and to deal with this various forms of the rubber rings used here were tried and also axial spring loading of the rubber joint by means of a wavy metal spring. Of the more successful forms of rubber rings tried was one suggested by Colonel

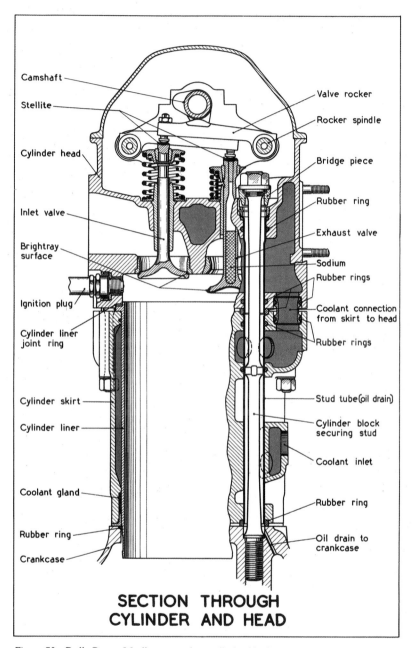

Camshaft

Stellite

Cylinder head

Inlet valve

Brightray surface

Ignition plug

Cylinder liner joint ring

Cylinder skirt

Cylinder liner

Coolant gland

Rubber ring

Crankcase

Valve rocker

Rocker spindle

Bridge piece

Rubber ring

Exhaust valve

Sodium

Rubber rings

Coolant connection from skirt to head

Rubber rings

Stud tube (oil drain)

Cylinder block securing stud

Coolant inlet

Rubber ring

Oil drain to crankcase

SECTION THROUGH CYLINDER AND HEAD

Figure 72   Rolls-Royce Merlin—two-piece cylinder block.

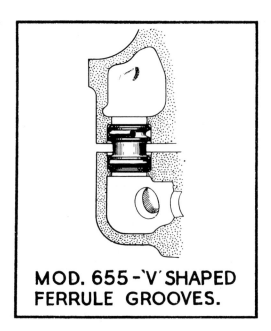

MOD. 655 - 'V' SHAPED
FERRULE GROOVES.

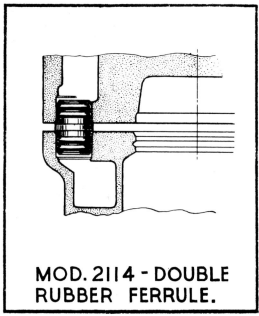

MOD. 2114 - DOUBLE
RUBBER FERRULE.

Figure 73 Rolls-Royce Merlin—cylinder head transfer
bobbins—various Mod standards.

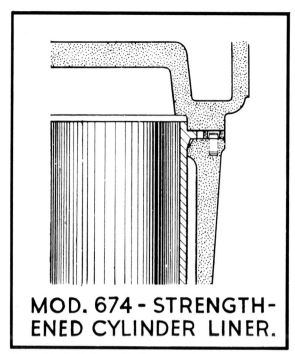

MOD. 674 - STRENGTH-
ENED CYLINDER LINER.

Figure 74   Rolls-Royce Merlin—strengthened cylinder liner.

Figure 75   Rolls-Royce Merlin—Harvey-Bailey (By)
sealing rings.

Barrington (Bn) which consisted of a series of moulded-in pockets providing additional barriers against leakage. The most successful one, however, both from the point of view of leakage prevention and also ease of manufacture, was one proposed by R W Harvey-Bailey (By) which consisted essentially of three rubber rings of circular cross section (75) joined together axially but moulded in flat form so that when the ring was fitted over the cylinder liner the defects arising from the mould joint did not occur at the contacts with the liner and the jacket skirt. With such a ring, when stretched over the liner the part which formed the inner ring during the moulding process in the flat was stretched more than the other two rings and this had to be dimensionally allowed for in the sectional diameters of the three rings, but once established caused no trouble in manufacture. A further difficulty at this joint was due to the fact that under piston loading the liner tended to move transversely within the bore of the jacket skirt, as relative expansion with temperature took place during engine running, and to deal with this an 'L' section steel ring (72) with a close clearance on the liner was inserted into the jacket skirt bore with its flange trapped between the lower face of the jacket and the crankcase mounting face. In this way the base of the liner was firmly held by friction against piston loading and the combination of these two designs proved to be a complete cure for the trouble at this location. Further design changes were introduced later on to improve conditions at the top joint so as to allow for increased engine ratings and increased times between overhaul. A method was evolved on development for measuring and comparing the leakage of gas from the top joint which gave trouble due to local overheating. To provide a larger surface area between liner flange and head and also to reduce the overhang of the loads arising from the main holding-down studs and the additional side studs, the basic diameter of the liner flange was increased by quite a large amount. This meant, of course, that the flange had to be cut back locally between adjacent cylinders and also to clear the main holding-down studs at the side studs, and all this added to the cost of production of the liner itself.

By eliminating all joint washers and the head recesses for these, the bottom face of the head could now be finished on a diamond miller to give a fine surface finish and at the same time save manufacturing costs on this component. All this proved to be very effective in reducing the amount of gas leakage at the joint face and therefore gave much improved conditions at this general location, particularly after long running hours in civil applications.

Various methods of directing the coolant flow through the jacket and head were tried but the best all-round compromise (76) was found to be by using a side rail for entry from the water pump near the base of the jacket, the rail having three flanged connections to the cored spaces in the jackets between adjacent cylinders. The coolant transfer ferrules between jacket and head referred to previously led from similar pockets into the head, and outlets from the head at the ends and in the centre were connected to a rail leading to the header tank.

Valves and valve gear

An enormous amount of development work was done on exhaust valves and seats to prevent localised burning of the former. The exhaust valves were, of course, sodium-cooled following a practice initiated during the Schneider Cup Race many years previously. The best combination of valve and seat was found to be the use of 'Stellite' material for the latter and a 'Brightray' coating on the seat of the former. The screwed-in valve seats, after being immersed in liquid air, were inserted by quickly spinning into position. This method gave a good interference fit remaining at the working temperatures

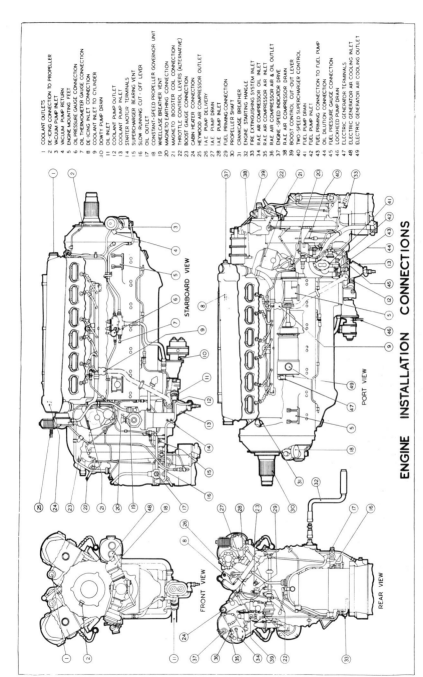

1 COOLANT OUTLETS
2 DE-ICING CONNECTION TO PROPELLER
3 VACUUM PUMP INLET
4 VACUUM PUMP RETURN
5 ENGINE MOUNTING FEET
6 OIL PRESSURE GAUGE CONNECTION
7 OIL THERMOMETER GAUGE CONNECTION
8 DE-ICING INLET CONNECTION
9 COOLANT INLET TO CYLINDER
10 DOWTY PUMP DRAIN
11 OIL INLET
12 COOLANT PUMP OUTLET
13 COOLANT PUMP INLET
14 STARTER MOTOR TERMINALS
15 SUPERCHARGER BEARING VENT
16 SLOW RUNNING CUT-OFF LEVER
17 OIL OUTLET
18 CONSTANT-SPEED PROPELLER GOVERNOR UNIT
19 WHEELCASE BREATHER VENT
20 MAGNETO EARTHING CONNECTION
21 MAGNETO BOOSTER COIL CONNECTION
22 THROTTLE CONTROL LEVERS (ALTERNATIVE)
23 BOOST GAUGE CONNECTION
24 CABIN HEATER CONNECTION
25 HEYWOOD AIR COMPRESSOR OUTLET
26 I.A.E PUMP DELIVERY
27 I.A.E PUMP DRAIN
28 I.A.E PUMP INLET
29 FUEL PRIMING CONNECTION
30 PROPELLER SHAFT
31 CRANKCASE BREATHER
32 ENGINE STARTING HANDLE
33 FIRE EXTINGUISHING SYSTEM INLET
34 R.A.E AIR COMPRESSOR OIL INLET
35 R.A.E AIR COMPRESSOR AIR INLET
36 R.A.E AIR COMPRESSOR AIR & OIL OUTLET
37 ENGINE-SPEED INDICATOR DRIVE
38 R.A.E AIR COMPRESSOR DRAIN
39 BOOST CONTROL CUT-OUT LEVER
40 TWO-SPEED SUPERCHARGER CONTROL
41 FUEL PUMP DRAIN
42 FUEL PUMP INLET
43 FUEL PRIMING CONNECTION TO FUEL PUMP
44 OIL DILUTION CONNECTION
45 FUEL PRESSURE GAUGE CONNECTION
46 LOCKHEED PUMP DRAIN
47 ELECTRIC GENERATOR TERMINALS
48 ELECTRIC GENERATOR AIR COOLING INLET
49 ELECTRIC GENERATOR AIR COOLING OUTLET

STARBOARD VIEW

PORT VIEW

FRONT VIEW

REAR VIEW

ENGINE INSTALLATION CONNECTIONS

Figure 76 Rolls-Royce Merlin 24 installation showing coolant inlet to cylinder (9)

91

attained by the head and seat and no trouble was experienced due to leakage or the seat becoming loose.

Earlier on, reference was made to the trouble experienced with severe wear of the type of valve gear used in conjunction with the ramp head. With the increase in hours run between services the valve gear rockers for the flat head used on the later marks of Merlin proved to have similar troubles, mainly with break-up of the cam follower pad on the rocker arm, due to overstressing arising from excessive unit loading. The situation was improved by using a greater depth of chromium on the rocker pad, initially to .006 in. and later to .012 in., but reliability also depended upon accurate control of the plating and grinding operations. It was apparently necessary under these loading conditions to provide a greater depth of hard material under the pad surface and this gave a considerable improvement in the condition of the follower pads after long running hours. A further improvement could have been obtained by the use of a larger base circle on the cam but this would have meant raising the camshaft centre-line which would have involved further changes in the camshaft drives with serious effects on interchangeability and also in the valve gear covers and engine cowlings and was not proceeded with.

Auxiliary gearboxes

As referred to previously on the question of aircraft auxiliary drives, it was decided that the best arrangement would be to mount all the aircraft auxiliaries on a separately mounted gearbox carried on the aircraft bulkhead. Such an arrangement made engine replacement in the aircraft much simpler as the only item to be disconnected was the actual drive from the engine, thus enabling all the various connections from the auxiliaries to the aircraft systems to be left undisturbed. It was decided that the auxiliary gearbox (77) itself would be designed and produced by the Rotol Co., which had been set up to produce propellers for Rolls-Royce and Bristol engines. After considerable investigation it was found that a simple drive from the engine (78) could be obtained by the provision of a mounting flange on the gearbox section of the supercharger drive. On this mounting flange was bolted a small casing containing a train of three gears, one of which protruded through a hole in the supercharger drive gear casing.

New engine types like the Griffon embodied this change from the start of production, but on the Merlin where there were installation interchangeability problems it was more difficult. The first Merlins (Mk 85) to feature auxiliary gearbox drives were for the Lancaster IV, which became known as the Lincoln, and used the new Rolls-Royce circular powerplant.

Variable-pitch propeller

Variable-pitch propellers began to come into use in the early life of the Merlin engine and reference has already been made earlier on to the provision of a drive for a constant speed unit for propeller operation. The first variable-pitch propellers available were of the Hamilton type originating in the United States and for the manufacture of which, in this country, a licence had been obtained by the de Havilland Co. For the operation of these it was necessary to provide high pressure oil supply to the propeller hub from the engine system via the constant speed unit and this was done through tubes carried within the propeller shaft engaging white-metalled bronze floating bushes carried in the rear of the reduction gear casing. In the case of the Hamilton airscrew, low pitch was

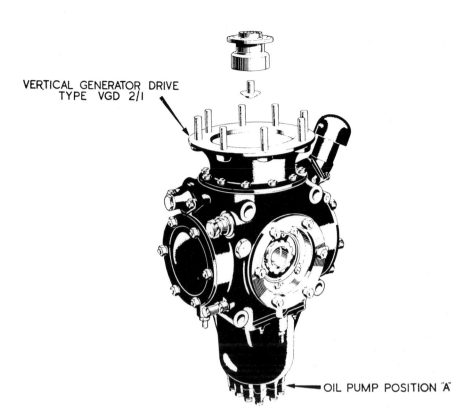

VERTICAL GENERATOR DRIVE
TYPE VGD 2/1

OIL PUMP POSITION "A"

Accessory gearbox, type AG. 4/8 (front view)

Figure 77 Rotol accessory gearbox.

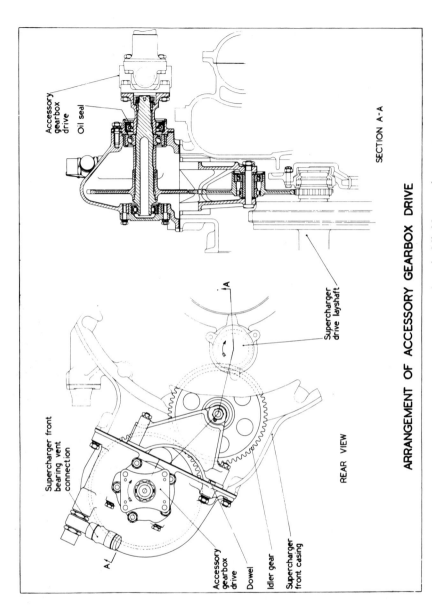

Accessory gearbox drive

Oil seal

SECTION A-A

Supercharger front bearing vent connection

A

Accessory gearbox drive

Dowel

Idler gear

Supercharger front casing

Supercharger drive layshaft

REAR VIEW

A

ARRANGEMENT OF ACCESSORY GEARBOX DRIVE

Figure 78   Rolls-Royce Merlin—accessory gearbox drives as used on the Mk 85 onwards.

obtained by bob-weights attached to the blade roots and oil pressure had therefore to be conveyed only to one side of the hydraulic piston operating the blade positions. A design of variable pitch hub had also been made by the Bristol Co., in which the hydraulic cylinder contained within the blade roots in the hub was double acting (**79, 80**). This eliminated the need for bob-weights on the blade roots but needed an oil feed to each side of the hydraulic operating piston, this latter feature requiring passage ways in the hub driving sleeve with the appropriate oil feed bushes. This hub design was later superseded by a design (**81**) emanating from Rolls-Royce and proposed by A G Elliott (E) in which the operating cylinder was moved into a position in front of the hub and operated the blade roots by means of connecting rods sliding through holes in the front part of the hub and links attached thereto onto the blade roots themselves. This arrangement enabled the hub to be much smaller in diameter with a smaller spinner and fitted in better with the requirements of the liquid-cooled engine as compared with the air-cooled. All design work and manufacture of this type of hub and also that of the constant speed unit associated with it, was later taken over by the Rotol Co. The design of the C.S.U.was based on the Hamilton unit with the valve controlling double-acting ports (**82**).

Two-stage supercharged engines

Fairly early on in the war we were visited by Rex Pierson, at that time Chief Designer of Vickers, to discuss a proposal in which he had interested the Air Ministry and the Air Force. This was for a high altitude version of the Wellington bomber which would be able to penetrate into the heart of Germany without heavy losses arising from enemy fighter action and anti-aircraft fire. In order to provide for the lengthy sorties over enemy territory that this would involve, it was necessary to provide a pressurised cabin for the pilot of which a suitable design had been evolved.

The requirement was for an ability to cruise at 30,000 ft and it would be necessary to provide an additional drive on the engine for a cabin blower.

In order to obtain the latter feature quickly and avoid too much redesign it was decided to use the Coffman starter type crankcase. Certain marks of Merlin had used the Coffman cartridge starter which cranked the engine via an extra pinion in the reduction gear. It was easy to adapt the crankcase and reduction gear to accept a cabin supercharger. The Company was already working on a two-stage supercharger to improve the power and altitude performance of the Merlin and this would meet the requirement to cruise at 30,000 ft.

The new supercharger (**83**) achieved two stages by mounting the two rotors on a single shaft, which had to be rigid to prevent whirling. The bearing arrangement followed normal practice, with a ball bearing at the front end to deal with both journal and thrust loads. The tail bearing was of the twin floating bush type as used on single-stage engines. The pressure ratio required to be developed within the supercharger was around 6:1 and this would entail very high inlet temperatures to the cylinders, with resulting effects on detonation and pre-ignition even with 100 octane fuel. To deal with this particular problem it was necessary to introduce an aftercooler (intercooler) between the supercharger outlet and the engine induction system.

Various methods were investigated, but it was found that the best all round solution would be provided by a heat exchanger, using water glycol mixture as the cooling medium. This was circulated by its own pump through a suitably mounted radiator. The design provided a very neat arrangement and permitted the aftercooler to be

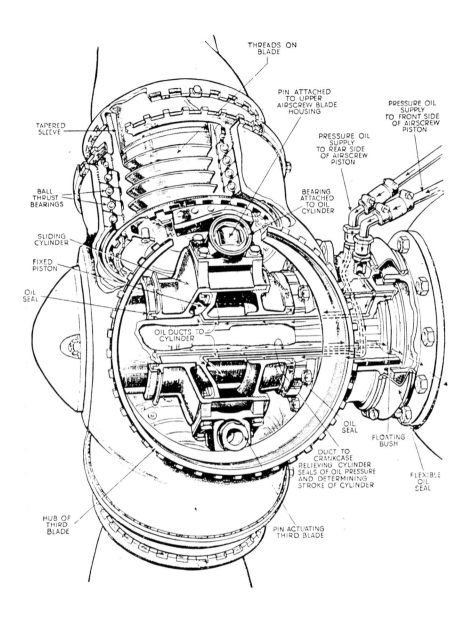

THREADS ON
BLADE

PIN ATTACHED
TO UPPER
AIRSCREW BLADE
HOUSING

PRESSURE OIL
SUPPLY
TO FRONT SIDE
OF AIRSCREW
PISTON

TAPERED
SLEEVE

PRESSURE OIL
SUPPLY
TO REAR SIDE
OF AIRSCREW
PISTON

BALL
THRUST
BEARINGS

BEARING
ATTACHED
TO OIL
CYLINDER

SLIDING
CYLINDER

FIXED
PISTON

OIL
SEAL

OIL DUCTS TO
CYLINDER

OIL
SEAL

FLOATING
BUSH

DUCT TO
CRANKCASE
RELIEVING CYLINDER
SEALS OF OIL PRESSURE
AND DETERMINING
STROKE OF CYLINDER

FLEXIBLE
OIL
SEAL

HUB OF
THIRD
BLADE

PIN ACTUATING
THIRD BLADE

Figure 79 The original type of Rotol 'internal cylinder' constant speed propeller unit with a pitch
range of 20°—Rotol being a joint company set up by Rolls-Royce and Bristol Aeroplane
Co. in June 1937.

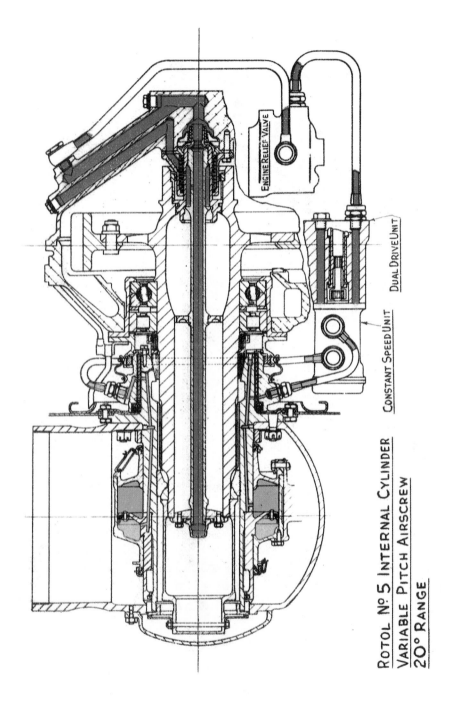

ROTOL Nº 5 INTERNAL CYLINDER
VARIABLE PITCH AIRSCREW
20° RANGE

ENGINE RELIEF VALVE

DUAL DRIVE UNIT

CONSTANT SPEED UNIT

Figure 80 Cross section of Rotol 'internal cylinder' constant speed propellor unit.

97

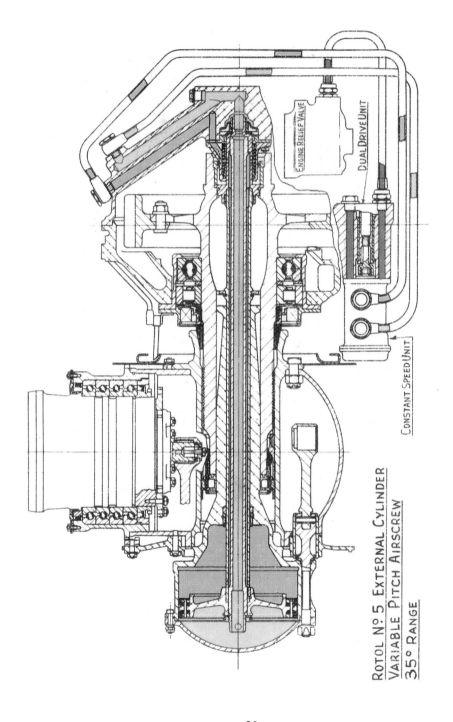

ROTOL NO. 5 EXTERNAL CYLINDER
VARIABLE PITCH AIRSCREW
35° RANGE

Figure 81 The later Rotol constant speed propellor unit with an 'external cylinder' and a pitch range of 35°.

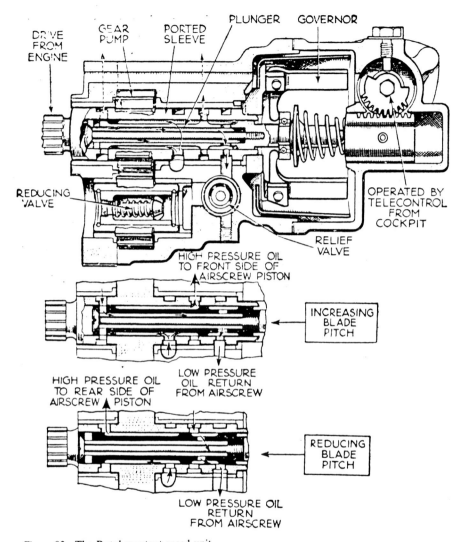

DRIVE FROM ENGINE

GEAR PUMP

PORTED SLEEVE

PLUNGER

GOVERNOR

REDUCING VALVE

OPERATED BY TELECONTROL FROM COCKPIT

RELIEF VALVE

HIGH PRESSURE OIL TO FRONT SIDE OF AIRSCREW PISTON

INCREASING BLADE PITCH

HIGH PRESSURE OIL TO REAR SIDE OF AIRSCREW PISTON

LOW PRESSURE OIL RETURN FROM AIRSCREW

REDUCING BLADE PITCH

LOW PRESSURE OIL RETURN FROM AIRSCREW

Figure 82 The Rotol constant speed unit.

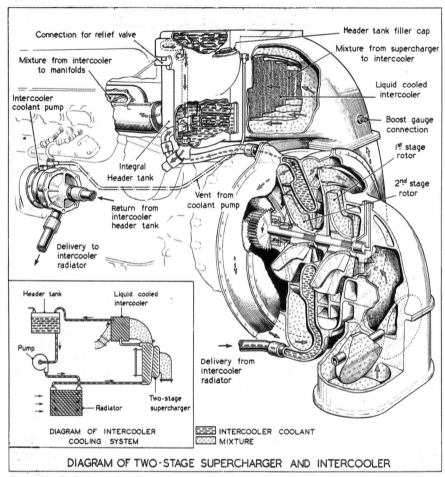

Connection for relief valve

Header tank filler cap

Mixture from supercharger to intercooler

Mixture from intercooler to manifolds

Liquid cooled intercooler

Intercooler coolant pump

Boost gauge connection

1st stage rotor

Integral Header tank

2nd stage rotor

Vent from coolant pump

Return from intercooler header tank

Delivery to intercooler radiator

Header tank

Liquid cooled intercooler

Pump

Delivery from intercooler radiator

Radiator

Two-stage supercharger

DIAGRAM OF INTERCOOLER COOLING SYSTEM

INTERCOOLER COOLANT
MIXTURE

DIAGRAM OF TWO-STAGE SUPERCHARGER AND INTERCOOLER

Figure 83 Rolls-Royce Merlin—two-stage supercharger and intercooler.

incorporated within the existing cowling lines of the powerplant. The position of the carburettor was retained on the inlet side of the supercharger and this, of course, reaped the additional advantage of the cooling provided by evaporation of the fuel as it passed through the compressor. The extra stage of supercharging increased engine length, which had to be catered for by modified engine mounts and associated items.

Unfortunately, the high altitude Wellington was abandoned after a number of aircraft had been built and did not see operational service over enemy territory. However, the two-stage Merlin (**84**) was highly successful in later marks of Spitfire, Mosquito and Mustang, and in heavy bombers, the Lancaster VI and Lincoln.

Suitable modifications had also to be made to the supercharger drive to enable it to handle the increased power to be transmitted. This was all accomplished within existing dimensions without any further increase in overall length beyond that required by the additional stage in the compressor.

On later marks of engine (Merlin 100 series) the rotor system (**85**) was redesigned to delete the tail bearing, its place being taken by an inter-stage roller bearing, leaving the first-stage rotor overhung. Apart from improving performance, this enabled single-point fuel injection into the eye of the supercharger to be used, superseding carburettors.

Figure 84   Rolls-Royce Merlin 66 with two-stage supercharger and Bendix injection carburettor.

Main bearing oil feed

The standard practice for supplying oil to the crankcase main bearings was by the use of a brazed-up assembly of steel piping attached to the main bearing blocks by banjo connections (**86**) and by a union at the pump end of the gallery connection. This assembly was subjected to fatigue failures due to the overhung nature of the assembly and the vibration to which it was subjected by its location in the crankcase. To overcome this a modified design (**87**) was introduced. This used a duralumin gallery pipe having outlets carried off machined facings on the lower face of the crankcase, oil feed holes being drilled from these facings to the main bearing blocks and thence by milled slots to the main bearing shells themselves. This design was very successful in eliminating the original trouble and the fact that there was slight leakage at the various joint faces, caused by the oil on its way to the bearings, was of no moment as this leakage occurred within the crankcase and in any case was small in relation to the volume of oil being passed.

101

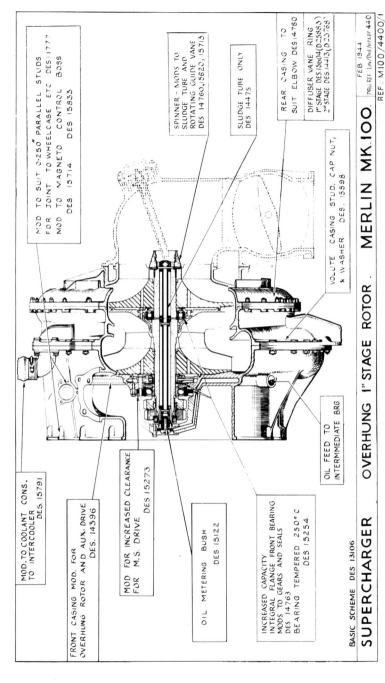

MOD. TO COOLANT CONS.
TO INTERCOOLER
DES. 15791

FRONT CASING MOD. FOR
OVERHUNG ROTOR AND AUX. DRIVE
DES. 14396

MOD FOR INCREASED CLEARANCE
FOR M.S. DRIVE
DES 15273

OIL METERING BUSH
DES 15122

INCREASED CAPACITY
INTEGRAL FLANGE FRONT BEARING
MODS TO GEARS AND SEALS
DES 14763
BEARING TEMPERED 250°C
DES 15254.

MOD TO SUIT 0.250" PARALLEL STUDS
FOR JOINT TO WHEELCASE ETC DES.11777
MOD TO MAGNETO CONTROL BOSS
DES 15714   DES 15833

SPINNER - MODS TO
SLUDGE TUBE AND
ROTATING GUIDE VANE
DES 14760,15620, 15713

SLUDGE TUBE ONLY
DES 14475

REAR CASING TO
SUIT ELBOW DES/4760

DIFFUSER VANE RING
1ST STAGE DES/5604(0.25893)
2 STAGE DES 14413(0.23768)

FEB 1944
MfRs. REF. LOW/DHI/MFKBF 440

REF: M100/4400/1

VOLUTE CASING STUD, CAP NUT,
& WASHER DES. 15598

OIL FEED TO
INTERMMEDIATE BRG

BASIC SCHEME DES 13106

SUPERCHARGER   OVERHUNG 1ST STAGE ROTOR.   MERLIN MK.100.

Figure 85   Rolls-Royce Merlin 100—two stage supercharger with overhung 1st stage.

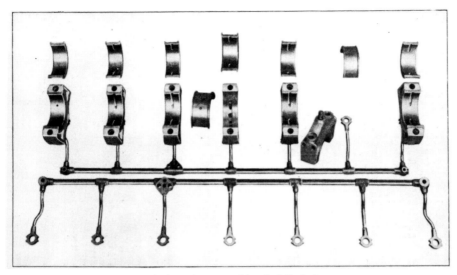

Figure 86 Rolls-Royce Kestrel—brazed up assembly of oil feed pipes.

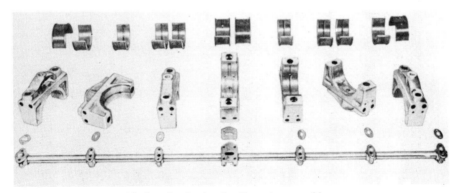

Figure 87 Rolls-Royce Merlin—duralumin oil gallery pipe assembly.

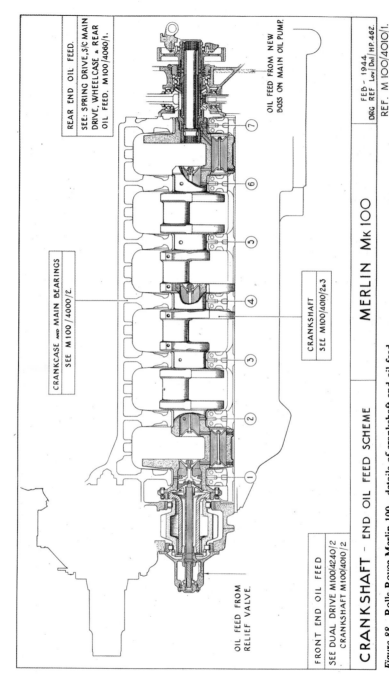

REAR END OIL FEED.

SEE: SPRING DRIVE, S/C MAIN DRIVE, WHEELCASE & REAR OIL FEED. M100/4060/1.

OIL FEED FROM NEW BOSS ON MAIN OIL PUMP.

CRANKCASE AND MAIN BEARINGS
SEE M100 / 4000 / 2.

CRANKSHAFT
SEE M100/4010/2&3

OIL FEED FROM RELIEF VALVE.

FRONT END OIL FEED
SEE DUAL DRIVE M100/4240/2
CRANKSHAFT M100/4010/2

CRANKSHAFT - END OIL FEED SCHEME   MERLIN MK100

FEB - 1944.
DRG REF Low/Drn/HP.462.

REF. M 100/4010/1.

Figure 88 Rolls-Royce Merlin 100—details of crankshaft end oil feed.

104

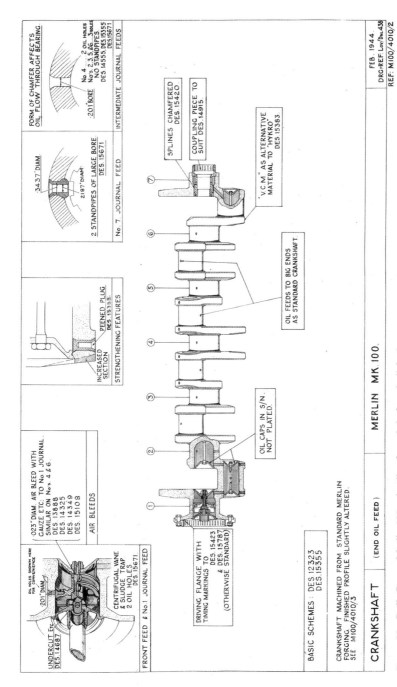

FORM OF CHAMFER AFFECTS OIL FLOW THROUGH BEARING.

No 4 ... 2 OIL HOLES
Nos. 2,3,5, &6. 3 HOLES
NO STANDPIPES
DES 14555, DES 15355
DES 15671

.201 BORE

INTERMEDIATE JOURNAL FEEDS

SPLINES CHAMFERED
DES 15420

COUPLING PIECE TO SUIT DES 14915.

34·37" DIAM.

2·187" DIAM.

2 STANDPIPES OF LARGE BORE
DES 15671

No. 7 JOURNAL FEED

'V.C.M.' AS ALTERNATIVE MATERIAL TO 'HYKRO'
DES 15383

OIL FEEDS TO BIG ENDS AS STANDARD CRANKSHAFT

INCREASED SECTION

PEENED PLUG
DES 15355.

STRENGTHENING FEATURES

OIL CAPS IN S/N. NOT PLATED.

·023" DIAM. AIR BLEED WITH GAUZE ETC: TO No.1 JOURNAL. SIMILAR ON Nos. 4 & 6.
DES 13888
DES 14325
DES 14349
DES 15108

AIR BLEEDS

OIL HOLES SHOWN HERE FOR CONVENIENCE

.201 DIAM.

CENTRIFUGAL VANE & SLUDGE TRAP
DES 15671

2 OIL HOLES

UNDERCUT F'g
DES 14687

FRONT FEED & No.1 JOURNAL FEED

DRIVING FLANGE WITH TIMING MARKINGS TO
DES.15423
& DES.15787
(OTHERWISE STANDARD)

BASIC SCHEMES : DES 12323
DES.15355

CRANKSHAFT MACHINED FROM STANDARD MERLIN FORGING. FINISHED PROFILE SLIGHTLY ALTERED. SEE M100/4010/3

CRANKSHAFT	(END OIL FEED)	MERLIN MK 100.

FEB. 1944.
DRG-REF: Lov/Dм.438
REF: M100/4010/2

Figure 89 Rolls-Royce Merlin 100—details of crankshaft end oil feed.

Attempts were made to reduce main oil flows with the object of lowering the amount of heat passed to the oil, thus enabling smaller and lighter oil coolers to be used in the aircraft installation. However, events proved that bearing reliability under the demands of wartime operation required larger total oil flows. An increase of 40% in flow, accompanied by some detail changes in main bearing oil grooves and extra oil holes in the crankpins, proved completely successful, while the extra splash this created improved piston cooling.

End-to-end crankshaft oil feed

A further improvement was gained by using the end feed oil system (**88, 89**), all the oil flow to the bearings passing through transfer tubes in the ends of the crankshaft, the hollow main journals and crankpins being interconnected by drillings within the crank webs. Small holes in the end bearing feeds, on the axis of rotation, allowed any air trapped in the oil system to escape and its effectiveness was demonstrated by special tests in which compressed air was induced into the oil system. In addition, standpipes were fitted in the end journals so that the crank acted as a centrifugal separator, trapping foreign matter that might be present in the oil. This system was adopted on Merlin 100 series and two-stage civil engines, which were noted for their excellent bearing condition, an improvement in general wear and, of course, a considerable reduction in the incidence of main bearing failures.

The feed into the front end of the crankshaft was achieved quite simply by means of a tube carried at each end in bronze bushes on the main bearing axis. At the rear a slightly more complicated arrangement had to be used, the feed taking place between a pair of bronze bushes riding on the outer member of the main spring drive to the auxiliaries and the supercharger, and thence into the rear of the crankshaft.

Flame traps

Reference to flame traps was made earlier, in dealing with the problems of backfires in the supercharger on the Kestrel. In the case of the Merlin it was found necessary to introduce flame traps in the induction system as boost pressures became higher and no further strengthening of the supercharger casings could be brought about. The flame traps (**31**) used on the Merlin were obtained from the Amal Co., and consisted of a rectangular frame into which packs of nickel silver thin plates were assembled to be edge-on to the direction of gas flow through the induction manifold. The flame traps were assembled into a machined recess in the inlet manifold near the port face. With a depth of plate of about an inch in the direction of gas flow these were found to be very effective in stopping the progress of a backfire beyond the cylinder port face and reduced significantly resultant pressures generated within the induction system. After considerable running the flame trap frames were found to work loose within the recess in the manifold because of vibration. This provided a leakage path for the flame round the exterior of the trap. Means had to be evolved for securing the trap firmly down to a ledge in the manifold by means of a number of small studs. Positive locking of the nuts on these had to be provided to prevent the possibility of these becoming loose and eventually being drawn into the cylinders.

Engine externals

For civil use there was much criticism of the Merlin engine as it had been developed during the war, the circumstances of this development during war-time involving the addition of various components which entailed the use of a considerable amount of external piping, mostly of the flexible variety, which had been likened by one civil customer to a "bucket of worms".

Extensive redesign was therefore made to eliminate wherever possible all external piping and in the end only one external pipe was left and this was the one connecting the oil pump discharge from the lower half of the crankcase to the oil pressure relief valve unit on the side of the crankcase. This particular pipe had been free of any trouble in the whole of the service experience on the Merlin, and any change to a flexible pipe in this location was inhibited by the close clearance of the engine mounting frame and on this basis the pipe continued in its old form, and continued to be trouble free.

We were also requested by civil operators to make provision for a readily accessible filter in the main oil supply and the best place for this was found to be as part of the relief valve unit. Considerable work was required on this to make the operation of removing the filter for inspection as easy as possible and at the same time guard against the possibility of the filter cap becoming open due to the effects of vibration.

Carburettor and fuel injection equipment

The carburettors fitted to the early Merlin engines were of RR design and followed the previous Kestrel practice, using two chokes side by side in order to achieve minimum engine length. In general, Claudel Hobson features were used and a manually variable main jet orifice was incorporated to provide for altitude control of mixture strength. The variable jet consisted of a conically seated valve provided with a lip of varying radius which by rotation could vary the effective size of the main jet, which consisted of a circular hole in the valve seating. In order to reduce the number of controls to be operated by the pilot, we were asked to provide the carburettor with automatic mixture control for altitude. For this purpose the S.U. company had designed a twin choke carburettor in which the size of the main jet orifice could be varied by a profiled needle which was attached to an aneroid bellows. The carburettor also had a secondary main jet, the area of which could again be varied by means of a profiled needle attached to a second aneroid bellows, which was subjected to engine boost pressure instead of ambient pressure. This arrangement gave mixture strength that was also dependent on boost pressure, giving weak mixture for cruising and a richer mixture at maximum boost pressure to inhibit detonation.

A carburettor of this type was made by the S.U. Co. (**90**), and found to perform very satisfactorily, both on the test bed and in flight. It was feared at one time that sticking of the profiled needles in their guides would prevent accurate axial movement, this was found not to be so, believed to be due to the general vibration experienced by these components in this location under running conditions. A competitive design was also prepared by Claudel Hobson and a unit made for test. To obtain automatic mixture control at altitude this carburettor was fitted with a variable main jet operated by a separate oil pressure operated servo unit which had been developed by them in conjunction with the R.A.E. at Farnborough. It was mainly this feature which led to this design being turned down in favour of the S.U. because it was feared that the introduction of an oil pressure operated servo might result in failure of engine oil pressure due to oil pipe failures. Development was therefore concentrated on the S.U. system.

It was later found in aerial combat with the German Air Force that under certain conditions, such as negative 'G', the Merlin would cut momentarily due to conditions in the float chamber. This did not occur with the German engines which were equipped

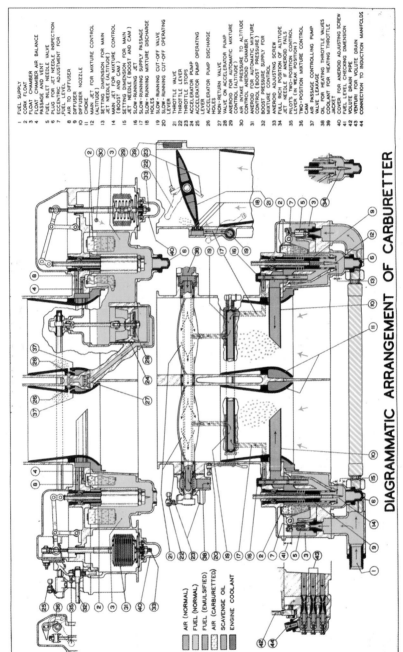

1 FUEL SUPPLY
2 CORK FLOAT
3 FLOAT CHAMBER
4 FLOAT CHAMBER AIR BALANCE PASSAGE AND VENT
5 FUEL INLET NEEDLE VALVE
6 PLUG FOR JET NEEDLE INSPECTION
7 ECCENTRIC ADJUSTMENT FOR FUEL LEVEL
8 AIR TO DIFFUSER
9 DIFFUSER
10 DIFFUSER NOZZLE
11 CHOKE
12 MAIN JET FOR MIXTURE CONTROL (ALTITUDE)
13 SETTING DIMENSION FOR MAIN JET NEEDLE (ALTITUDE)
14 MAIN JET FOR MIXTURE CONTROL (BOOST AND CAM)
15 SETTING DIMENSION FOR MAIN JET NEEDLE (BOOST AND CAM)
16 SLOW-RUNNING JET
17 SLOW-RUNNING SUPPLY PASSAGE
18 SLOW-RUNNING MIXTURE DISCHARGE HOLES
19 SLOW-RUNNING CUT-OFF VALVE
20 SLOW-RUNNING CUT-OFF OPERATING LEVER
21 THROTTLE VALVE
22 THROTTLE LEVER
23 THROTTLE STOP
24 ACCELERATOR PUMP
25 ACCELERATOR PUMP OPERATING LEVER
26 ACCELERATOR PUMP DISCHARGE HOLES
27 NON-RETURN VALVE
28 VALVE ON ACCELERATOR PUMP
29 ANEROID FOR AUTOMATIC MIXTURE CONTROL (ALTITUDE)
30 AIR INTAKE PRESSURE TO ALTITUDE CONTROL ANEROID CHAMBER
31 ANEROID FOR AUTOMATIC MIXTURE CONTROL (BOOST PRESSURE)
32 BOOST PRESSURE SUPPLY FOR MIXTURE CONTROL
33 ANEROID ADJUSTING SCREW
34 FULL RICH POSITION OF ALTITUDE JET NEEDLE IF ANEROID FAILS
35 PILOT'S TWO-POSITION CONTROL LEVER (IN WEAK POSITION)
36 TWO-POSITION MIXTURE CONTROL CAM
37 AIR PASSAGE CONTROLLING PUMP VALVE LEAKAGE
38 OIL FOR HEATING THROTTLE VALVES
39 COOLANT FOR HEATING THROTTLE JACKET
40 COVER FOR ANEROID ADJUSTING SCREW
41 FUEL LEVEL CHECKING DIMENSION
42 VOLUTE DRAIN PIPE
43 VENTURI FOR VOLUTE DRAIN
44 CONNECTION TO INDUCTION MANIFOLDS

AIR (NORMAL)
FUEL (NORMAL) OR
FUEL (EMULSIFIED)
AIR (CARBURETTED)
SCAVENGE OIL
ENGINE COOLANT

DIAGRAMMATIC ARRANGEMENT OF CARBURETTER

Figure 90 Rolls-Royce Merlin—diagram of S U carburettor.

108

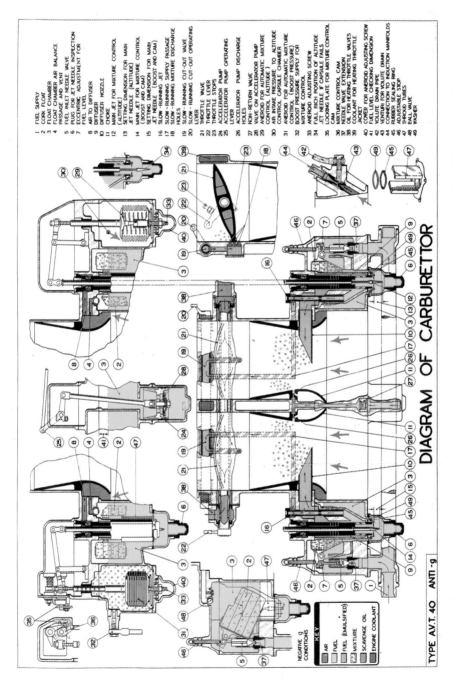

Figure 91 Rolls-Royce Merlin—S U carburettor with anti-G modification developed in conjunction with RAE, Farnborough.

109

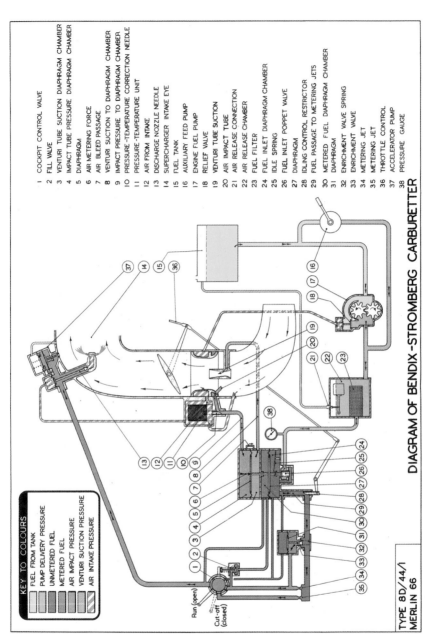

DIAGRAM OF BENDIX-STROMBERG CARBURETTER

KEY TO COLOURS

- FUEL FROM TANK
- PUMP DELIVERY PRESSURE
- UNMETERED FUEL
- METERED FUEL
- AIR IMPACT PRESSURE
- VENTURI SUCTION PRESSURE
- AIR INTAKE PRESSURE

1 COCKPIT CONTROL VALVE
2 FILL VALVE
3 VENTURI TUBE SUCTION DIAPHRAGM CHAMBER
4 IMPACT TUBE PRESSURE DIAPHRAGM CHAMBER
5 DIAPHRAGM
6 AIR METERING FORCE
7 AIR BLEED PASSAGE
8 VENTURI SUCTION TO DIAPHRAGM CHAMBER
9 IMPACT PRESSURE TO DIAPHRAGM CHAMBER
10 PRESSURE-TEMPERATURE CORRECTION NEEDLE
11 PRESSURE-TEMPERATURE UNIT
12 AIR FROM INTAKE
13 DISCHARGE NOZZLE NEEDLE
14 SUPERCHARGER INTAKE EYE
15 FUEL TANK
16 AUXILIARY FEED PUMP
17 ENGINE FUEL PUMP
18 RELIEF VALVE
19 VENTURI TUBE SUCTION
20 AIR IMPACT TUBE
21 AIR RELEASE CONNECTION
22 AIR RELEASE CHAMBER
23 FUEL FILTER
24 FUEL INLET DIAPHRAGM CHAMBER
25 IDLE SPRING
26 FUEL INLET POPPET VALVE
27 DIAPHRAGM
28 IDLING CONTROL RESTRICTOR
29 FUEL PASSAGE TO METERING JETS
30 METERED FUEL DIAPHRAGM CHAMBER
31 DIAPHRAGM
32 ENRICHMENT VALVE SPRING
33 ENRICHMENT VALVE
34 METERING JET
35 METERING JET
36 THROTTLE CONTROL
37 ACCELERATOR PUMP
38 PRESSURE GAUGE

TYPE 8D/44/1
MERLIN 66

Run (open)
Cut-off (closed)

Figure 92 Rolls-Royce Merlin—diagram of Bendix-Stromberg carburettor.

110

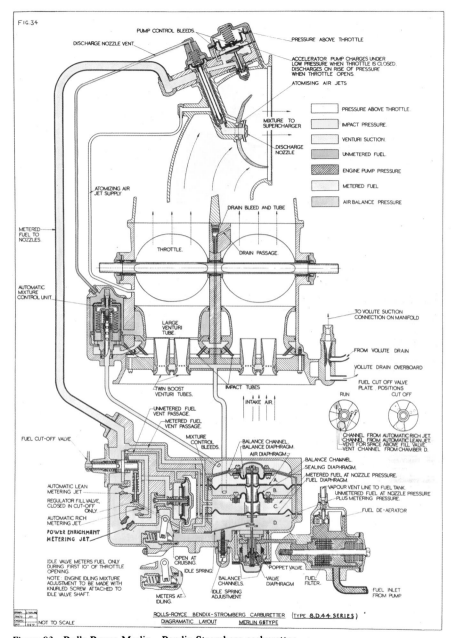

Figure 93 Rolls-Royce Merlin—Bendix Stromberg carburettor.

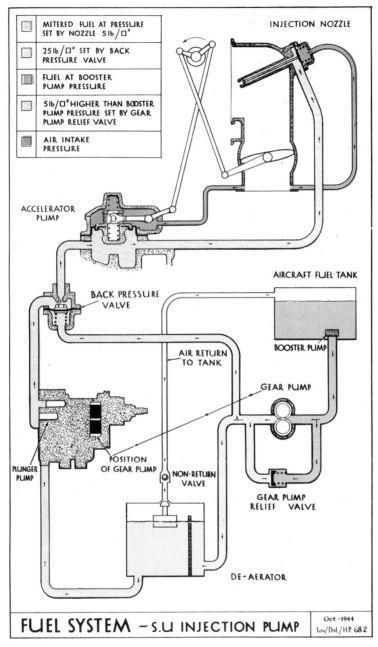

Figure 94 Rolls-Royce Merlin—fuel system for S U injection pump.

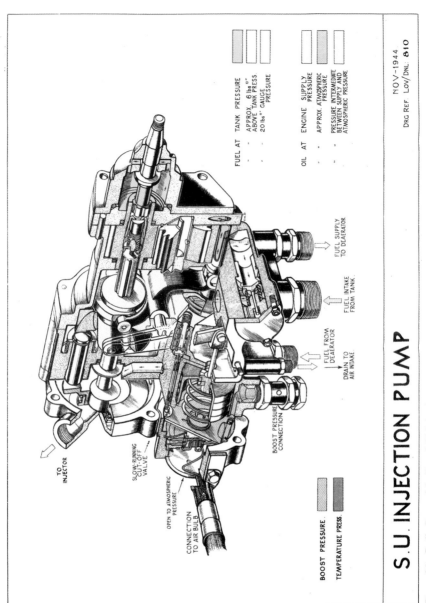

S.U. INJECTION PUMP

FUEL AT TANK PRESSURE

,, — APPROX. 6 lbs □" ABOVE TANK PRESS
,, — 20 lbs □" GAUGE PRESSURE

OIL AT ENGINE SUPPLY PRESSURE

,, — APPROX. ATMOSPHERIC PRESSURE
,, — PRESSURE INTERMEDIATE BETWEEN SUPPLY AND ATMOSPHERIC PRESSURE

NOV-1944
DRG. REF. LOV/DNL. 810

FUEL SUPPLY TO DEAERATOR

FUEL INTAKE FROM TANK.

FUEL FROM DEAERATOR

DRAIN TO AIR INTAKE

BOOST PRESSURE CONNECTION

TO INJECTOR

SLOW-RUNNING CUT-OFF VALVE

OPEN TO ATMOSPHERIC PRESSURE

CONNECTION TO AIR BULB

BOOST PRESSURE.

TEMPERATURE PRESS.

Figure 95 Rolls-Royce Merlin—S U injection pump.

113

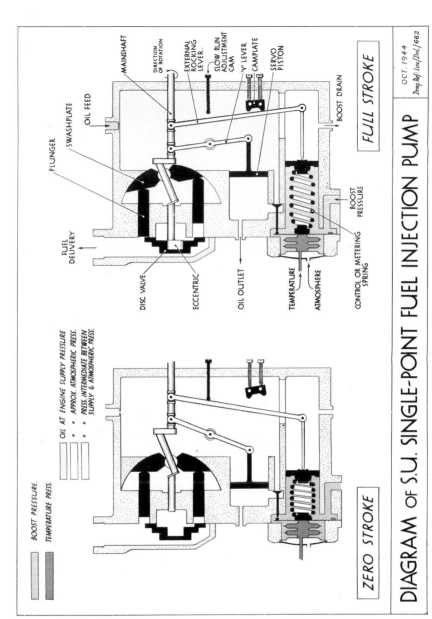

Figure 96   Rolls-Royce Merlin—diagram of S U injection pump.

114

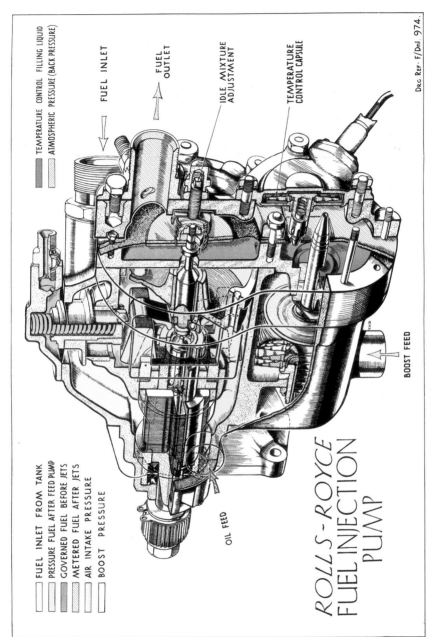

TEMPERATURE CONTROL FILLING LIQUID
ATMOSPHERIC PRESSURE (BACK PRESSURE)

FUEL INLET

FUEL OUTLET

IDLE MIXTURE ADJUSTMENT

TEMPERATURE CONTROL CAPSULE

DRG. REF. F/DNI. 974.

BOOST FEED

OIL FEED

ROLLS-ROYCE
FUEL INJECTION PUMP

FUEL INLET FROM TANK
PRESSURE FUEL AFTER FEED PUMP
GOVERNED FUEL BEFORE JETS
METERED FUEL AFTER JETS
AIR INTAKE PRESSURE
BOOST PRESSURE

Figure 97 Rolls-Royce Griffon—Rolls-Royce fuel injection pump.

115

with direct fuel injection, advantage of this being taken by the German pilots in combat. To deal with this problem a negative 'G' carburettor was designed which provided a diaphragm controlled fuel supply to the carburettor as a replacement for the normal float and needle. This proved unsuccessful in service trials and an anti 'G' version of the S.U. carburettor (91) was developed, with modified valving in the float chamber. This worked satisfactorily and was in use to the end of the war on both single and two stage engines. In the meantime flight testing at Farnborough had shown that by putting a restrictor in the fuel line to the carburettor to limit maximum fuel flows, the hazard of the 'rich cut' with the standard carburettor under negative 'G' conditions could be much reduced and engines were modified in the field. Although the Germans' use of direct petrol injection into the cylinders avoided this particular trouble, their system had some serious disadvantages compared with the carburettor system. One of the main disadvantages was that it did not take advantage of the temperature drop which occurred to the mixture as it passed through the supercharger and therefore did not gain the advantage of increased volumetric efficiency due to this, and this had a major effect on power development. The other disadvantage of the direct injection system was its complication and the possibility of nacelle fires caused by injection pipe failures.

The next move on the Merlin was to use the Bendix type of carburettor (92,93), which supplied fuel by a low pressure spray into the first stage of the supercharger. Fuel metering was achieved with diaphragm controls and this carburettor was used on certain types of single and two-stage Merlins and two-stage Griffons. There had been good experience on the Bendix instrument on Packard built Merlins.

There followed direct injection (94) of fuel into the eye of the supercharger through the medium of a special injection pump, by which fuel supply was controlled by engine speed and boost pressure. This unit (95) had been designed by the S.U. Company and consisted of a main supply gear pump with a metering control by means of axial plungers, whose stroke could be controlled by a variable angle swash plate (96). With this arrangement the chokes normally used for a carburettor were eliminated, and the throttle became a large rectangular plate, thus reducing pressure losses into the supercharger inlet. On later types this was further improved by the introduction of a Corliss throttle.

With single point injection into the eye of the supercharger fuel distribution was quite even. Full advantage was taken of the temperature drop of the mixture passing through the supercharger due to evaporation of the fuel.

Rolls-Royce further developed this principle, using a gear pump only (97). In this case engine control was obtained by using the pressure drop in the fuel supply passing through a fixed orifice. Although much cheaper to manufacture it was not used on production Merlins. It was, however, fitted to later marks of two-stage Griffons and the single-stage version used on the Shackleton.

More on valves and valve gear

Some difficulties were experienced with the various valve gears used on the Merlin. On the first series of Merlin engines using the ramp head the valve gear design was based on a system using a single camshaft carried within a long tunnel member with openings at the top for access to the rocker followers. These were of the reversing type with the rocker bearing situated between the follower and the valve actuating tappet. This arrangement was thought to be good as it enabled the cams to run in an oil bath to ensure good lubrication with the followers. However, it was soon found that, in spite of the good lubrication conditions achieved by this, the followers had a very short life due to break-up of the follower surface.

116

No improvement was found to be made by providing flash chromium plating on the follower surface. It was also noted that the degree of break-up experienced depended on the direction of rotation of the camshaft relative to the rocker, and it was concluded from this that friction at the follower cam contact added to, or subtracted from, the contact load and therefore determined which rockers would fail first. To avoid this condition, special cams were designed which resulted in them being of an asymmetric shape. In addition, in order to save weight, the whole of the gear was redesigned eliminating the tunnel feature, as it had also been concluded that the oil bath feature provided by this gave no advantage. The performance of this gear was also disappointing, partly because the asymmetrically shaped cams provided, at some points, a reduced relative radius of curvature at the point of contact with the follower and for this reason increased the local surface unit loading. However, further development of this gear was stopped by the changeover to the flat pancake head instead of the ramp head. The valve gear associated with this, based on the design used on the Kestrel, performed much more satisfactorily although trouble was still experienced, after long running hours, with break-up of the follower pad surfaces on the rockers. To deal with this problem two lines of development were considered. The first was to make a substantial increase in the base circle diameter of the camshaft so as to improve the relative radius of curvature of cam and follower pad and thus reduce the unit loading at the contact point. In order to achieve this it was necessary to raise the camshaft centre-line, and to avoid changes to other engine components, such as the wheelcase, it was necessary for the raising of the camshaft to take place along the line of the camshaft inclined drive, which was not parallel to the cylinder centres. This introduced difficulties due to the resulting changes in the leverage ratio in the rockers themselves. Raising the camshaft also had the disadvantage of increasing the engine nacelle cowling diameter at the front end and the resultant increase in drag. This particular development was therefore not followed up and no designs were produced on these lines or components made for test.

The second line of action investigated was based on the fact that the condition of the follower pads at the front end of the engine were always worse than those at the back end, and it was deduced from this that the cause might be due to varying angular velocity of the cams over the period of rotation. This would arise due to the fact that the torque driving a 6-cylinder camshaft reverses during the period of rotation and therefore any slack in the drive affects the angular velocity of the cams. In addition, the torsional flexibility of the camshaft itself would mean that the effects of this would be additive at the front end compared with the rear. To deal with this effect, some 6-cylinder car engines had been provided with an additional 6-lobe cam and a spring-loaded follower, which had the effect of producing a constant unidirectional torque to drive the camshaft, and this was said to be quite successful in operation. The alternative way of producing a similar effect was to position an additional cam on each cylinder centre line contacting a spring-loaded rocker, again with the objective of providing a constant unidirectional torque.

Neither of these proposals reached fruition. Satisfactory reliability was obtained using .012 in. depth of hard chromium on the rockers, accompanied by accurate control of all the manufacturing processes.

THE GRIFFON

Following the success of the 'R' engine a derated version known as the Griffon (**98**) was tested in 1933. It was not continued with at the time, but shortly before the war it was realised that there would be advantages in having a larger engine than the Merlin that would fit into existing installations. It was felt that it would be needed to compete with the bigger radial engines then under development. The obvious choice was to do a redesign of the Griffon, using the 'R' engine bore and stroke, and the Griffon I (**99**) ran in the Experimental in November 1939.

The first production version, the Griffon II (**100**), went into service with the Firefly in 1942. In order to keep the overall dimensions within the limits imposed by application to existing fighter aircraft, considerable investigation took place in a re-arrangement of the engine components, so that any increase in overall length could be kept to a minimum. In order to achieve this it was decided to move both camshaft drives and part of the supercharger drive to the front end of the engine (**101**). The first part of the step-up of the supercharger drive was carried out by means of a gear mounted on the front end of the crankshaft driving a pinion below it in one piece with a long shaft and running in bearings carried in the lower half to the rear end of the engine. The second part of the step-up was completed through clutches and gear trains providing for moderate and full supercharger ratios as alternatives. The long shaft being kept to a fairly small diameter provided the requirements for a spring drive without any additional components. The second part of the step-up gear so provided did not give a balanced drive to the supercharger rotor as was at one time thought to be essential under the

Figure 98 The original Rolls-Royce Griffon—a derated 'R' engine.

Figure 99   Rolls-Royce Griffon I.

Figure 100   Rolls-Royce Griffon II.

119

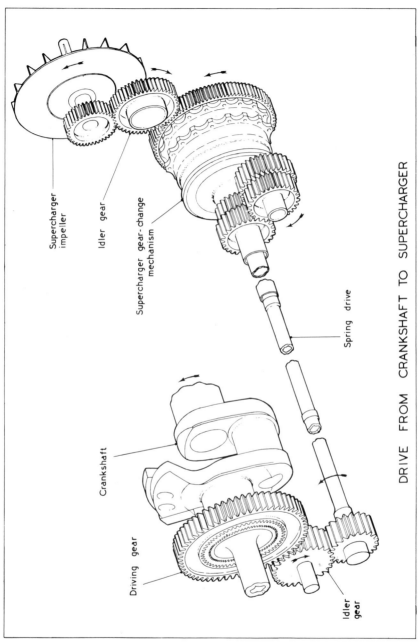

Supercharger impeller

Idler gear

Supercharger gear-change mechanism

Spring drive

Crankshaft

Driving gear

Idler gear

DRIVE FROM CRANKSHAFT TO SUPERCHARGER

Figure 101 Rolls-Royce Griffon—The initial supercharger drive from front of crankshaft and two-speed oil operated clutches at the rear.

high speed conditions under which the rotor bearings had to run, but it was found that the ball bearing used for this application ran quite satisfactorily under these conditions. The operation of the two clutches initially followed a practice introduced by the Bristol Company. In this the clutches were engaged by hydraulic pressure generated by oil trapped in the revolving clutch housing through the medium of a large diameter piston and, although this worked satisfactorily initially, it was soon found that quantities of sludge were centrifuged out and eventually prevented proper movement of the piston. The design, therefore, had to be modified by providing the load to the clutches from revolving bob-weights, the fulcrum of which was positioned such that the bob-weights, in travelling over-centre, could apply load to either clutch. Release and engagement of the bob-weights was obtained from a fixed oil pressure operated piston contained within the shaft carrying this mechanism.

This arrangement of supercharger drive was not liked for various manufacturing reasons and was later replaced on following marks of Griffon engines by a design (102) in which both step-up trains were carried at the rear end of the engine. In this case the main driving wheel was carried on plain bearings on a rearward extension inserted into the crankshaft and was driven by a spring drive shaft which projected into the hollow end of the supercharger rotor shaft but with a good clearance from the latter. During development, failure was experienced of the outer part of the spring drive shafts, the manufacture of which involved a trepanning operation which itself gave rise to a pronounced stress concentration. This particular trouble was overcome by making the piece in two portions which avoided the trepanning operation, the two parts being united through a press fit and the medium of radial taper pins held in position by local peening. This solution proved to be a complete cure for this trouble.

In order to obtain the absolute minimum in overall length a single magneto was also used. Suitable magnetos of this type had been designed by both of the magneto supply companies, on the basis that the reliability obtained formerly by having two independent magnetos, as on the Merlin, could be obtained by the use of a single instrument. This had two separate magnetic circuits which would give the same electrical reliability as the use of two separate units. On this unit, instead of the normal moveable contact breaker for varying the ignition timing, which had the disadvantage of giving a varying spark discharge at the plug terminals, a fixed contact breaker was used. Variation of the spark timing being achieved by means of a variable timing device in the drive to the magneto (103). This was achieved through the medium of an oil operated servo piston moving a sliding sleeve in the drive having helical splines and responsive to movement of the throttle control. The magneto itself was mounted on top of the reduction gear casing and gave a very neat arrangement of electrical harness branching out to the two cylinder banks. All of these changes gave a very cobby appearance to the engine and enabled it to be installed in a later mark of the Spitfire even with the further addition of two-stage supercharging and the use of aftercooling. A third drive ratio for the supercharger was subsequently obtained to give both greater powers and higher altitude performance, without compromising the low altitude characteristics of the engine.

121

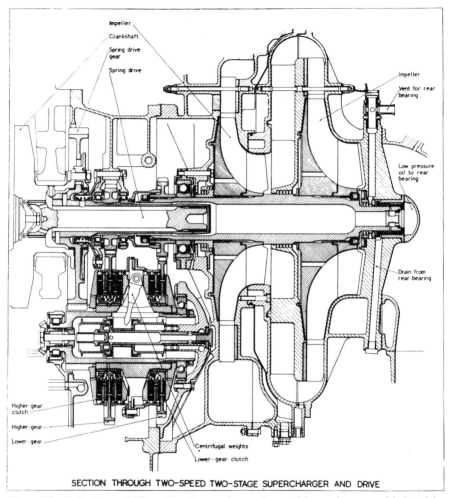

Impeller
Crankshaft
Spring drive gear
Spring drive
Impeller
Vent for rear bearing
Low pressure oil to rear bearing
Drain from rear bearing
Higher·gear clutch
Higher·gear
Lower·gear
Centrifugal weights
Lower·gear clutch

SECTION THROUGH TWO-SPEED TWO-STAGE SUPERCHARGER AND DRIVE

Figure 102   Rolls-Royce Griffon—The change of supercharger drive to the rear and bob-weight operation of the clutch.

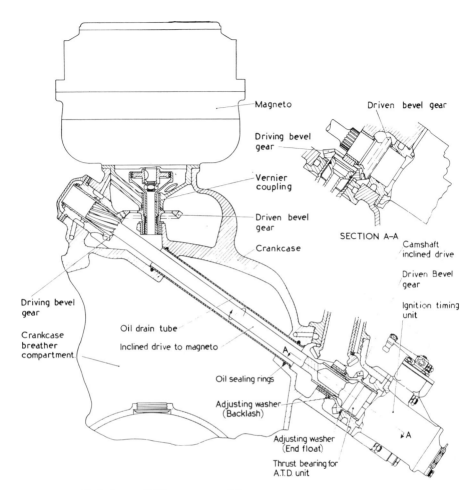

Magneto

Driving bevel gear

Vernier coupling

Driven bevel gear

Crankcase

Driven bevel gear

SECTION A-A

Camshaft inclined drive

Driven Bevel gear

Ignition timing unit

Driving bevel gear

Crankcase breather compartment

Oil drain tube

Inclined drive to magneto

Oil sealing rings

Adjusting washer (Backlash)

Adjusting washer (End float)

Thrust bearing for A.T.D. unit

Figure 103   Rolls-Royce Griffon—magneto drive.

123

LEFT- AND RIGHT-HAND TRACTOR MERLINS

During the later stages of the war a requirement arose for a version of the Merlin (**104**) with reversed rotation of one propeller in a twin engined plane called the de Havilland Hornet. This was an aircraft based on the Mosquito but with higher wing loading and having lower drag engine nacelles. The reversed rotation of one propellor cancelled the torque reaction of the other on the aircraft structure and its associate effect on aircraft handling during take-off, particularly on carrier applications. It was decided to achieve the reversed rotation by the insertion of an idler pinion in the reduction gear (**105**) and the initial experience of this showed serious difficulties resulting in serious local overheating at the tooth contact. The cause of this was eventually traced to lack of oil at the tooth contacts and special oil injection jets had to be introduced into the space between the gears to ensure that oil reached the loaded surfaces of the teeth. In order to achieve an engine nacelle of reduced drag, the water pump was removed from its normal position at the bottom of the wheelcase and fitted to the side of the crankcase using a drive initially provided for a generator.

Figure 104   Rolls-Royce Merlin 131.

124

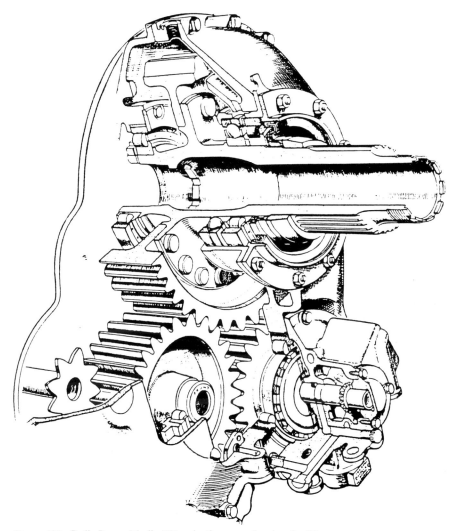

Figure 105 Rolls-Royce Merlin 131 reduction gear showing the idler.

CONTRA-ROTATING PROPELLERS

A contra-rotating reduction gear for use with a contra-rotating propeller was designed for both the Merlin and the Griffon. This followed the practice employed on the Merlin, but using two spur trains, one of which had an idler gear to give the required reverse rotation. The gear was used on a small batch of Merlin 140s for the twin engine Short Sturgeon for the Royal Navy.

Although a few Griffons were built with contra-rotating reduction gears (**106**) on a flight development basis for the Spitfire and Spiteful and their Naval developments, the more common use was in the Griffon (**107**) for the 4-engined Shackleton, a maritime reconnaissance aircraft.

An early trouble experienced on the Griffon was severe galling on the rear teeth of the coupling between the crankshaft and the reduction gear pinion, which was much more severe than on the corresponding parts on the Merlin. Various schemes were tried to improve this condition including the use of a diaphragm plate type of coupling instead of the toothed ring. This, however, suffered from local severe fretting which it was thought might lead to fatigue failure and was therefore abandoned. An alternative scheme tried using an intermediate ring having internal and external teeth engaging the crankshaft toothed ring on its outer diameter and the reduction gear coupling on its inner (**108**). This gave a considerable improvement although the trouble was never completely eliminated.

A special mounting frame was also designed for use with this engine incorporating flexible rubber mountings of the Metalastik type and was used in the engine power plant for the Shackleton aircraft in which the Griffon engine was installed.

Some later marks of Griffon were equipped with fuel injection into the eye of the supercharger, using the Rolls-Royce injection pump as referred to earlier.

Further designs for a two-speed reduction gear incorporating an intermediate epicyclic gear between the crankshaft and reduction gear pinion, in order to improve further the aircraft performance, were also completed but did not receive service application. However, by this time the application of the jet engine to fighter aircraft was beginning to dominate the field.The development of the cylinder block for the Griffon engine followed that of the Merlin, although at any one time the standard of development was behind that of the Merlin. One feature on the Merlin, the use of an inclined facing for the rocker cover joint in order to clear auxiliary drive provisions at the rear end, was unnecessary on the Griffon since from the start this engine was provided with a drive for a separate auxiliary gearbox.

In this case, therefore, the rocker cover joint face remained parallel with the lower face of the cylinder head. The valve gear and the valves themselves also followed the practice on the Merlin. It should also be recorded that the single magneto with separate magnetic circuits proved to be a reliable unit in service and the use of such a unit was therefore completely justified.

The Griffon was the first production engine to feature the end feed lubrication system, to be followed by the Merlin 100 series later in the war.

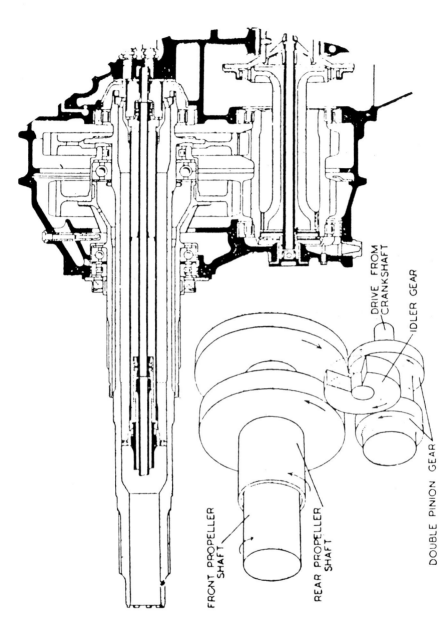

DRIVE FROM CRANKSHAFT

IDLER GEAR

DOUBLE PINION GEAR

FRONT PROPELLER SHAFT

REAR PROPELLER SHAFT

Figure 106 Rolls-Royce Griffon 83—Contra-rotating reduction gear—used in Supermarine Spitfire 21 and Spiteful and Martin Baker MB5.

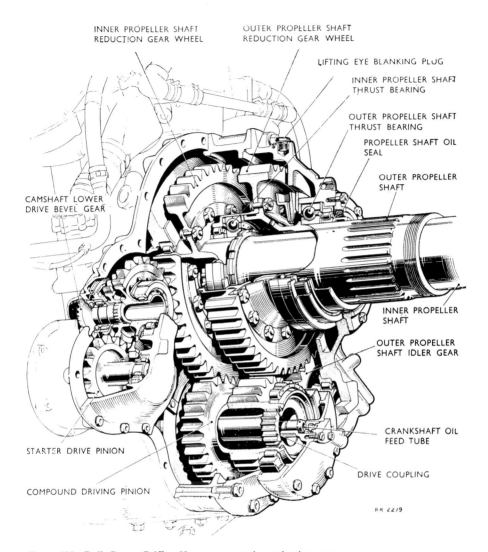

INNER PROPELLER SHAFT
REDUCTION GEAR WHEEL

OUTER PROPELLER SHAFT
REDUCTION GEAR WHEEL

LIFTING EYE BLANKING PLUG

INNER PROPELLER SHAFT
THRUST BEARING

OUTER PROPELLER SHAFT
THRUST BEARING

PROPELLER SHAFT OIL
SEAL

OUTER PROPELLER
SHAFT

CAMSHAFT LOWER
DRIVE BEVEL GEAR

INNER PROPELLER
SHAFT

OUTER PROPELLER
SHAFT IDLER GEAR

CRANKSHAFT OIL
FEED TUBE

STARTER DRIVE PINION

DRIVE COUPLING

COMPOUND DRIVING PINION

RR 2219

Figure 107 Rolls-Royce Griffon 58—contra-rotating reduction gear.

128

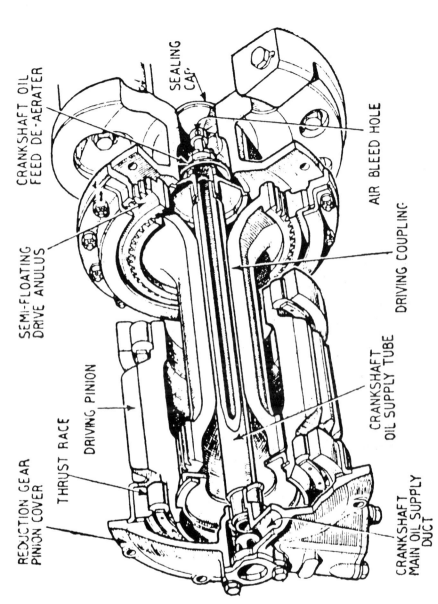

CRANKSHAFT OIL
FEED DE-AERATER

SEALING CAP

SEMI-FLOATING
DRIVE ANULUS

AIR BLEED HOLE

DRIVING COUPLING

REDUCTION GEAR
PINION COVER

THRUST RACE

DRIVING PINION

CRANKSHAFT
OIL SUPPLY TUBE

CRANKSHAFT
MAIN OIL SUPPLY
DUCT

Figure 108 Rolls-Royce Griffon 65—semi-floating coupling between crankshaft and reduction gear.

THE EAGLE 22

When consideration was given to the provision of a more powerful engine than the Griffon it was felt that a simple scale-up of the dimensions for a 12-cylinder 'V' engine would lead to combustion chamber dimensions which would make it difficult to deal with detonation as the result of increased flame front travel. This led to the conclusion that it would be necessary to have a larger number of smaller cylinders. The obvious choice for this was the 'X' form engine using 24 cylinders, a route which had been followed previously in the case of the Vulture engine. This had been found to have a number of serious drawbacks, not the least of which was the anchoring of four pistons to a common big end. One attractive arrangement for 24 cylinders was the use of an 'H' with two separate crankshafts (**109**), the latter feature avoiding the big end difficulties referred to above and enabling the use of blade and forked connecting rods as used on the 'V' engine. The 'H' form had already been used on the Napier Sabre engine, the drive from the two crankshafts being united through the propeller reduction gear (**110**).

It was decided to follow this route to provide an engine of around 3500 hp. In following the general layout of the Sabre considerable simplification was made in several areas, where to us it seemed there was unnecessary complication. This included the drives to the sleeve valves (**111**), which had also been adopted in the design. It was well recognised that at long lives the exhaust valve seats in poppet valve engines suffered from the effects of highly leaded fuels. Both Bristol and Napier had concentrated their efforts on sleeve valves and this was an opportunity for Rolls-Royce to gain further experience.

Supercharging followed Merlin and Griffon practice, being of the two-speed two-stage type. The first run of the engine was in March 1944 and it was first flown in the Westland Wyvern in December 1946. This was a creditable performance, but not without problems, which included piston ring and junk ring (**112**) difficulties. The installation in the Wyvern was somewhat fortuitous, because this aircraft was intended to use the Armstrong Siddeley Python propeller turbine. This engine was late and to meet the flight programme there was a short production run of Eagle 22s, the name given to the new type (**113,114**). The rapid development of gas turbines for fighter aircraft towards the end of the war meant that fighters in which the Eagle could have been installed were not proceeded with. Rolls-Royce had also produced a large propeller turbine, the Clyde, and one was test flown in a Wyvern.

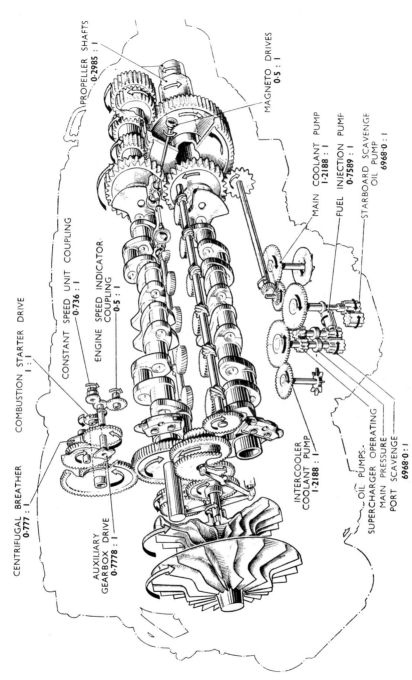

PROPELLER SHAFTS 0.2985 : 1

MAGNETO DRIVES 0.5 : 1

MAIN COOLANT PUMP 1.2188 : 1

FUEL INJECTION PUMP 0.7589 : 1

STARBOARD SCAVENGE OIL PUMP 6968.0 : 1

CENTRIFUGAL BREATHER 0.777 : 1

COMBUSTION STARTER DRIVE 1 : 1

CONSTANT SPEED UNIT COUPLING 0.736 : 1

ENGINE SPEED INDICATOR COUPLING 0.5 : 1

AUXILIARY GEARBOX DRIVE 0.7778 : 1

INTERCOOLER COOLANT PUMP 1.2188 : 1

OIL PUMPS— SUPERCHARGER OPERATING MAIN PRESSURE PORT SCAVENGE 6968.0 : 1

Figure 109 Rolls-Royce Eagle 22—arrangement of two separate crankshafts.

131

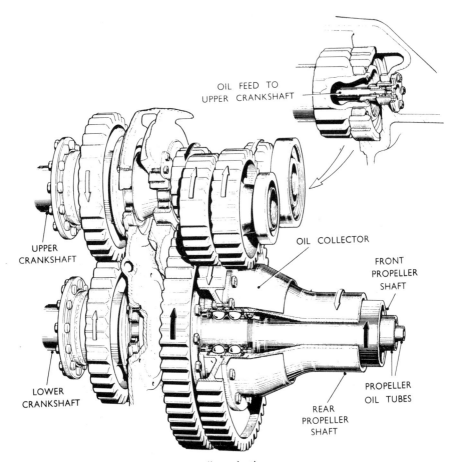

OIL FEED TO
UPPER CRANKSHAFT

UPPER
CRANKSHAFT

OIL COLLECTOR

FRONT
PROPELLER
SHAFT

LOWER
CRANKSHAFT

PROPELLER
OIL TUBES

REAR
PROPELLER
SHAFT

Figure 110 Rolls-Royce Eagle 22—propeller reduction gear.

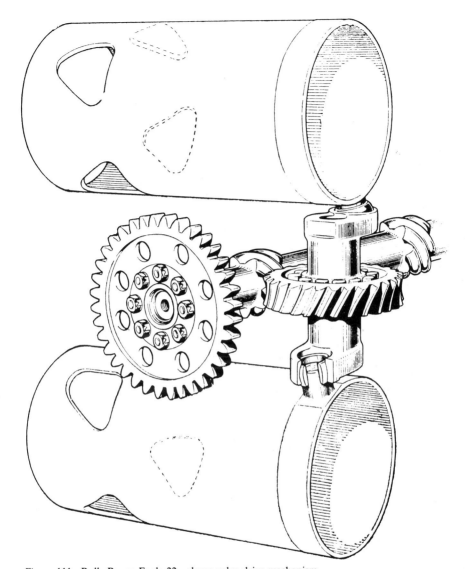

Figure 111 Rolls-Royce Eagle 22—sleeve valve drive mechanism.

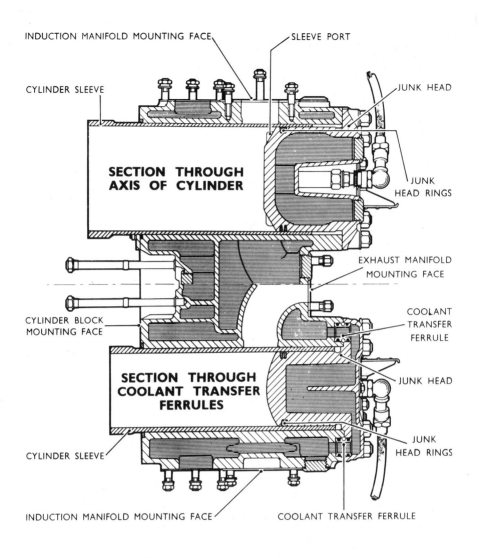

INDUCTION MANIFOLD MOUNTING FACE

SLEEVE PORT

CYLINDER SLEEVE

JUNK HEAD

SECTION THROUGH AXIS OF CYLINDER

JUNK HEAD RINGS

EXHAUST MANIFOLD MOUNTING FACE

COOLANT TRANSFER FERRULE

CYLINDER BLOCK MOUNTING FACE

JUNK HEAD

SECTION THROUGH COOLANT TRANSFER FERRULES

JUNK HEAD RINGS

CYLINDER SLEEVE

INDUCTION MANIFOLD MOUNTING FACE

COOLANT TRANSFER FERRULE

 COOLANT

Figure 112 Rolls-Royce Eagle 22—section through cylinder block showing junkhead and rings.

Figure 113 Rolls-Royce Eagle 22.

Figure 114 Rolls-Royce Eagle 22.

THE VULTURE

During the early development stages of the Merlin a requirement arose for a much more powerful engine for a twin-engined bomber aircraft later known as the Manchester. For this a power equivalent to twice that of the developed Kestrel engine was required and this led to the design of a 24-cylinder engine (115) with 4 banks of cylinders of Kestrel dimensions. In order to obtain the optimum firing order for such an arrangement it was decided that the angle between cylinder banks should be 90°, and the problem immediately arose as to how to deal with the big end. On the Eagle XVI engine this problem had been side-stepped by the use of normal blade and fork rods carried side-by-side on a common crank pin but this had the disadvantage of different cylinder spacings for the upper and lower blocks. In order to achieve all the 4 pistons on the same centre-line it was necessary to anchor the 4 pistons to a common big end bearing. At the time that this problem arose, an engine called the Exe was being designed by A J Rowledge and this used 24 cylinders of a similar 'X' form, but air-cooled and using sleeve valves. Due to the difficulty of providing normal bolting methods on a big end of this type, a design had been evolved in which the normal form of bolting was used on one side of the big end and cap, whereas on the other side a hinged joint was provided between cap and rod. This was formed by a series of interleaved lugs through which assembly was completed by a shear pin. All this was necessary on the master rod side of the big end because of the difficulty of providing normal bolting. The advantage of this type of composite construction was that it was still possible to provide a nip on the bearing shell for the big end by means of the two bolts provided.

On the Exe engine with this form of construction it was found that the use of the hinged joint on one side of the big end meant that no transmission of any bending moment could take place at the joint. This affected the mechanical rigidity of the big

Figure 115 Rolls-Royce Vulture II.

136

VULTURE STAR UNIT

BUTTING TYPE CONNECTING ROD TO DES 2724.

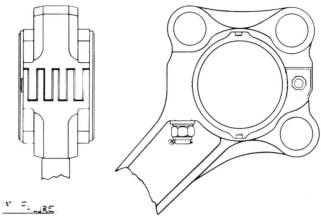

1st FAILURE.

CONNECTING ROD INTER-LEAVING LUGS FAILED AT ABRUPT CHANGE OF SECTION
RUNNING TIME ANALYSIS UP TO FAILURE POINT AS SHEWN BELOW

RUNNING TIME OF THE ABOVE CONNECTING ROD

R P M	2850		2700	2750		2800
B M E P LBS/□"	0 -140	.40 - .80	.40 - 80	C - .140.	40 -.80	0 -.40
TIME	99 - 32	0 - 3.	1 - 00	0 - 20	0 - 28	0 - 39

R P M	2850		3000	3200
B M E P LBS/□	0 -140	40 - 80	0 -140	0 -140
TIME	9 -19	7- 41	0 - 26	0 - 05

TOTAL RUNNING TIME - 120 HRS. 1 MIN.

R MILNER
17-9-37

Figure 116   Rolls-Royce Vulture—connecting rod with hinged joint.

VULTURE STAR UNIT.

NON BUTTING TYPE CONNECTING ROD TO DES. 3488

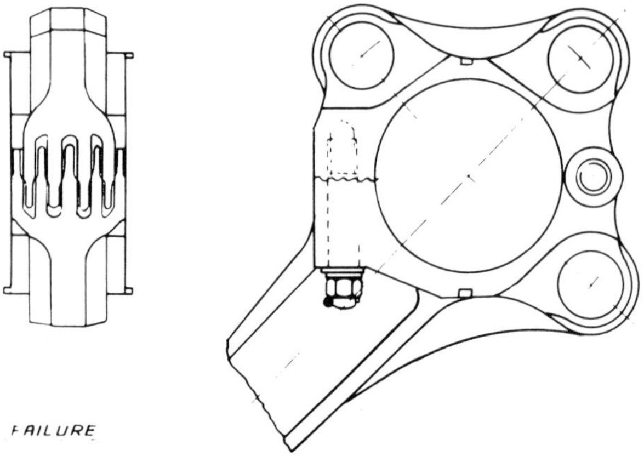

2 ND FAILURE

CONNECTING ROD STUDS FAILED DUE TO FATIGUE FRACTURE. RUNNING TIME ANALYSIS UP TO FAILURE POINT AS SHOWN BELOW.

RUNNING TIME OF THE ABOVE CONNECTING ROD.

R.P.M.	0 - 2600	2700	2750	2800	2850
B.M.E.P. LBS / □"	0-140	0-140	0-140	0-140	130
HRS. MIN.	9-54	0-30	0-10	0-32	2-02

13 HRS. 08 MINS. RUNNING TIME BEFORE BEING INSPECTED.

R.P.M.	0-2600	2600	2600	2200	3200
B.M.E.P. LBS / □"	0-140	143	155	156	122
HRS. MIN.	5-16	0-10	0-8	0-12	0-15

TOTAL RUNNING TIME 19 HRS. 9 MINS.

E.R. MILNER
17. 9. 37.

Figure 117 Rolls-Royce Vulture—connecting rod with modified hinged joint.

end, allowing frettage to take place between the rod and bearing shell leading eventually to fatigue failures.

On the Vulture an attempt was made to reproduce the effect of the bolted joint by allowing the hinge lugs on the cap to bottom in the gaps between the lugs on the master rod side (116,117). Manufacturing difficulties made it hard to obtain a pre-loading condition similar to that obtained with a bolted joint and this arrangement was therefore not very satisfactory from this point of view.

On the Exe engine it was eventually found that it was possible to get in a more normal bolted construction on the master rod side provided that the bolts were kept shorter than normal for bolts on this sort of application. This design (118) was eventually followed on the Vulture, special care being taken during assembly to obtain the correct stretch of the bolt during tightening by means of a direct measurement of stretch of the bolt during this process. With the realisation that the big end construction was likely to be the 'achilles heel' of the connecting rod assembly which would require a lot of development running without being interfered with by other engine troubles, it was decided to build what was known as a star unit. This is a section of four cylinders of the engine running as a unit on the test bed, and by this means a large number of development hours was obtained on this particular assembly.

In order to save weight it had also been decided to use battery ignition instead of magnetos, but it eventually proved too difficult to obtain satisfactory and reliable contact breaker and distributor units and we had therefore to revert to the use of two 24-cylinder magnetos. This entailed considerable revision of the drives at the front end to provide for this. For the cylinder blocks a construction similar to the Kestrel was used but, as the spacing between cylinder axes had to be greater as determined by the crankshaft, big end and main bearing requirements, this allowed a better spacing of the cylinder holding-down studs and the use of side saddle studs as followed on the Buzzard and Griffon. There was, however, one difficulty with this construction in that the higher piston side thrust imposed by the master rod, due to articulation of the other rods, caused shuffling of the liner flange on the crankcase facing. Had the engine gone into volume production, this would have proved a serious difficulty with extended running in service. Some consideration was also given in fact to the use of Merlin size cylinders as cylinder spacings were virtually the same on both types. The use of the two-piece construction as used on the Merlin, with the addition of a flanged close fitting collar trapped between the cylinder block and crankcase, might have dealt satisfactorily with this trouble. Of course the use of cylinder dimensions of Merlin proportions would have opened the way to further power development had development of the Vulture engine continued.

The propeller reduction gear (119) used on the Vulture took the form of a back gear using four layshafts and bringing the propeller shaft in line with the crankshaft. The layshafts were also used to provide the drive through bevels to the appropriate camshaft. In order to obtain equal loading on each layshaft the latter were provided with a flanged mounting of the layshaft gear in the first train, the bolting up of which was achieved under torque loading by reaming the fitting bolt holes in situ and this method proved quite satisfactory. Later on, to save weight for this unit, an epicyclic gear was designed and made for this application but did not reach the production stage before the project was stopped. The provision of a camshaft drive from the reduction gear at the front end of the engine gave a steadier drive to the camshaft but this was somewhat adversely affected by the additional slack caused by the use of a bevel-cum-spur final drive. This was to avoid the increased diameter of the engine cowling at the front end which would

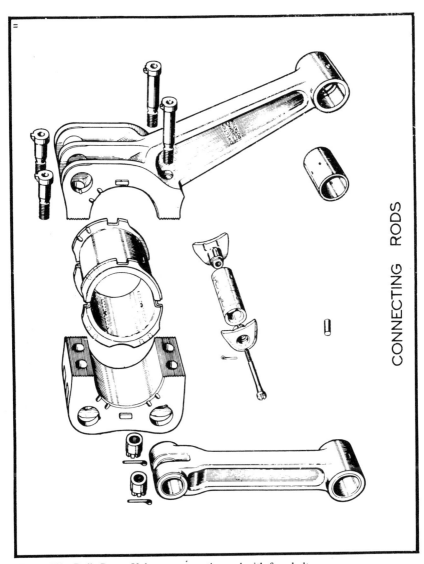

CONNECTING RODS

Figure 118 Rolls-Royce Vulture—connecting rod with four bolts.

140

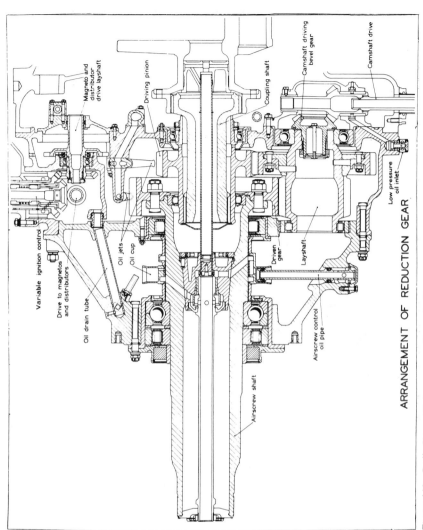

Figure 119 Rolls-Royce Vulture—propeller reduction gear.

ARRANGEMENT OF REDUCTION GEAR

Magneto and distributor drive layshaft

Driving pinion

Coupling shaft

Camshaft driving bevel gear

Camshaft drive

Low pressure oil inlet

Driven gear

Layshaft

Airscrew control oil pipe

Airscrew shaft

Oil jets

Oil cup

Oil drain tube

Drive to magnetos and distributors

Variable ignition control

141

have been required with the use of a larger diameter bevel gear mounted directly on the camshafts. However, following experience on the first two Vulture engines, the decision was taken to accept the increased engine diameter and to use the large bevel gear (120).

A serious trouble arose on the first production engines due to main bearing failures which were eventually traced to the top and bottom halves of the main bearings being built out-of-line. The bolting together of the two crankcase halves was achieved by what were known as cross-bolts which were positioned normal to the cylinder facing in order to deal directly with the explosion loadings arising from the cylinder blocks. These bolts being slightly staggered fore and aft to clear one another where they cross on the split line. Although a step was provided in the joint face between the halves of the crankcase to align them, this was not sufficient to prevent transverse slight relative movement applied at 45° through the joint face and dependent on the order of tightening of the bolts. The condition was slightly improved by imposing a rigid tightening order but was finally cured by the provision of cylindrical dowels, in the form of 'cheeses', which were large enough in diameter to allow the cross-bolts to pass through them; this also provided for location of the dowel endwise. With this modification (121) no further main bearing trouble was experienced.

One item of interest was the burning out of certain cylinder blocks as a result of the breakdown in the coolant circulation. The Vulture had two coolant pumps in parallel, with the result that one pump could get a complete breakdown in flow due to cavitation at its inlet, whilst the other pump maintained full flow. This effect was investigated by making the two pumps in a transparent material and the solution was to balance the inlet pressures to the two pumps by introducing a balance pipe (122).

Unfortunately in service as the engine of the Manchester bomber (123), a number of connecting rod bolt failures occurred. As a result several aircraft were lost causing a crisis in Bomber Command. It was this problem and the decision to use 4 Merlins instead of 2 Vultures, leading to the highly successful Lancaster (124), that caused the Vulture to be stopped, as the great power potential of the Merlin was then being appreciated.

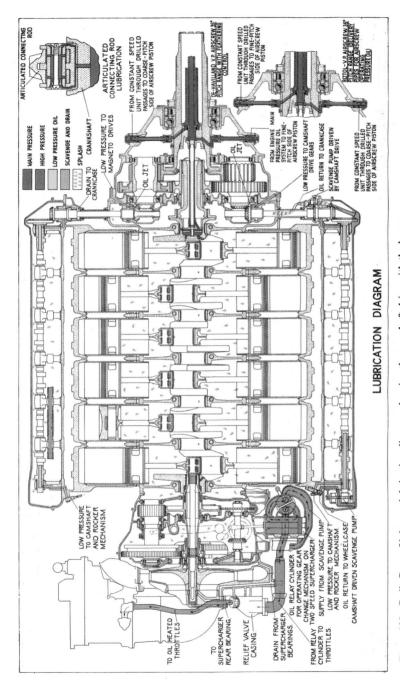

Figure 120 **Rolls-Royce Vulture**—lubrication diagram showing the camshaft drive with the larger diameter bevel gear.

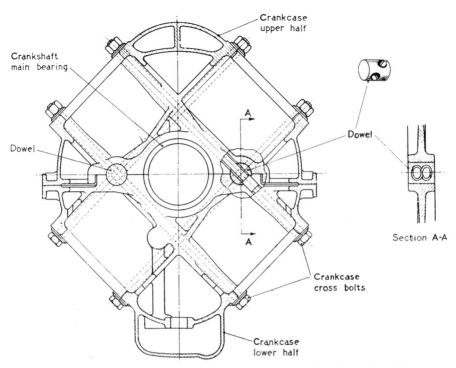

Figure 121 Rolls-Royce Vulture—cross section of crankcase showing cross bolts and dowels.

144

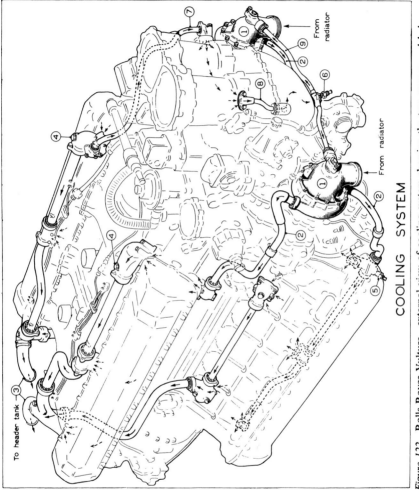

COOLING SYSTEM

Figure 122 Rolls-Royce Vulture—external view of cooling system showing the two pumps and balance pipe.

Figure 123 The Avro Manchester—showing the installation of the Rolls-Royce Vulture.

Figure 124 The Avro Lancaster powered by four Rolls-Royce Merlins.

THE EXE

In the early 1930s Rowledge had a serious illness which kept him away for a number of years. On his recovery it was decided not to bring him back into the main development programmes but he was given a free hand to design an engine on the lines which he considered it would be best to follow for future engine types. For this he decided to adopt the 'X' arrangement of cylinders and in order to keep the size of cylinders down to ease detonation problems he decided on the use of 24 cylinders in this form. At that time considerable successful development work had been done by the Bristol Company on the use of a sleeve valve instead of the normal poppet valve, in order to avoid the difficulties then being experienced with the latter due to valve seat troubles arising from the use of leaded fuels. He therefore chose this type of valve gear in conjunction with air cooling, which was also a feature of the Bristol design. An attraction of air cooling was that it avoided the troubles associated with water cooling and the installation difficulties arising therefrom. The 'X' arrangement of cylinders allowed the use of air pressure cooling in which the cooling air was admitted through a suitable opening in the engine cowling below the propeller shaft centreline. This air passing out between

Figure 125 Rolls-Royce Exe.

147

the cylinders to the spaces in the side 'V' from which it was evacuated rearwards. The arrangement gave an excellent distribution of the cooling air to all parts of the cylinders. The sleeve drives were obtained by longitudinal shafts driven off the reduction gear and carried in bearings at the side of the crankcase, each shaft providing drives through spiral gears to the sleeve drive cranks. The connecting rods were of the type using a master rod with the other three pistons connected through articulated rods, the big end bearing itself being split and bolted up with four bolts in its final arrangement. For the reduction gear to the propeller shaft Rowledge initially proposed a simple arrangement using a single pinion driving an internally toothed annulus gear on the propeller shaft, this arrangement giving the minimum offset position of the propeller shaft above the centre of area of the engine as viewed from the front. The problem of providing bearings for the crankshaft driven pinion was solved by using a rigid steel housing bolted to the front end of the crankcase which carried the fore and aft bearings for the pinion, but it was necessary for the propeller shaft gear to be overhung. The latter feature and the difficulty of providing sufficient rigidity in the annulus gear itself made the attainment of satisfactory bedding at the tooth contact surfaces difficult to obtain and for this reason this type of gear had to be abandoned in favour of the normal type of spur reaction gear as used on the Merlin.

This resulted in a considerable increase in the offset of the propeller shaft from the engine centreline. However, this feature helped the inducement of the cooling air for the cylinders by it taking place at a larger radius of the propeller blades. The engine (**125**) was rated at 1150 hp at take-off. It was installed at Hucknall in a Fairey Battle for flight test, but shortly after the outbreak of war the Exe was abandoned to allow more effort on Merlin development and production. Used as a communication aircraft during the war the Battle continued to fly, the Exe proving quite reliable. A larger version of the Exe, known as the Pennine, was designed and an engine was testbed run early in 1945, after which the project was stopped.

Some parallel work was done on a liquid-cooled version of the Exe engine. An experimental 4-cylinder 'star' unit was constructed, using steel cylinders with fabricated steel water jackets. These jackets proved to be very prone to cracking, so the cylinders were redesigned in cast aluminium. A main engine was produced and tested, but as with the air-cooled engine work was discontinued on the outbreak of war.

THE CRECY

In the continued drive for more power in less space and for less weight, we turned our attention to the two stroke cycle and the following is an extract from a paper given by Cyril Lovesey at the 11th Sir Henry Royce Memorial Lecture in 1966. "I well remember a typical remark from Dr S G Hooker who described a 4-stroke engine as one with 'one stroke to produce power and three strokes to wear it out'".

The original project was for a diesel two-stroke but the Air Ministry of that time directed that it should be designed as a fuel injection-spark ignition engine. This project was carried out in close collaboration with Ricardo who had built up a lot of experience on this subject on single-cylinder units. The Crecy (**126,127**) had a bore/stroke of 5.1 in/6.5 in, giving a displacement of 26 litres. It had a design rating of 1400 hp.

Work on the petrol injection version started in 1939 and the project was terminated early in 1945. This 90° 'V' sleeve valve engine proved a very complex and difficult undertaking. As often happens, many mechanical problems were encountered during main engine running that had not been foreshadowed during the development of individual components. One item I recall was the high torsional vibration stresses in the supercharger drive, to overcome which a freewheel device was tried. Other serious problems were main engine vibration, piston and sleeve cooling, all contributing to a complicated design.

Figure 126   Rolls-Royce Crecy.

Figure 127 Rolls-Royce Crecy.

In summary, the great contribution of Rolls-Royce to the war effort was the Merlin, which was successful in so many roles, with the Griffon as a back-up. While the other piston engines described provided useful information and enabled different design philosophies to be evaluated, they were supplanted by the Company's interest in the gas turbine, which took over from the Merlin.

APPENDIX

BIOGRAPHICAL NOTES

Arthur Alexander Rubbra

Notes on his early life and background by his son, Colin Rubbra

1. **Parents:** Father - Edmund James Rubbra, Born 1871, Died 1947

    Mother - Mary Jane, nee (Bailey ?), Born 1872 (?), Died 1942

His father had a business as a watch, clock and jewellery repairer. His mother apparently used to have a beautiful singing voice, and sang in the choir of the Primrose Hill Methodist church at Northampton, of which they were staunch members.

2. Origins of the Name

'Rubbra' must be one of the rarest surnames in England; at the moment only some dozen people bear the name. Almost certainly it has originated from corruption of place name 'Ruborough' in Somerset [literal meaning -'rough hill'], which also occurs in Devon and Somerset as Roborough and Rowberrow. Research has shown that the family first appears in Northampton early in the 1700s, was noted as coming from Somerset, and that one early spelling of the name was 'Ruborow'. Early members of the family in the 18th century included a master carpenter, a whitesmith, and a cabinet maker.

There is still another branch of the original family which spells its name 'Rubra'.

3. Birth

My father was born October 29th 1903, the second son. His elder brother, Charles Edmund, was born in May 1901. At the time the family were living in [address not known] Northampton.

4. Early Days

Whether my grandmother had secretly wished for a little girl, or whether it was perhaps normal fashion in the early 1900s, we do not know, but there is a photograph of my father at the age of about $2\frac{1}{2}$ looking like a little girl in pinafore and apron!

5. Boyhood

One of his earliest passions which remained with him to the end of his life was steam engines. He showed an early aptitude for drawing, and naturally, steam engines were the favoured subject. We have a remarkably good and detailed drawing of a L.N.W.R engine made when he was just 7! He spent many happy hours watching trains with his friend Bill Hurry at Blisworth, to the west of Northampton, on the main London-Crewe line and also, no doubt, on Northampton station itself, watching the performance of starting a Webb compound!

One other interest which remained with him throughout his life was clocks, perhaps naturally in view of his father's work. Certainly, the premises at 51 Overstone Road, Northampton, where the family eventually settled, were fascinating to a small boy, as I remember from pre-war visits. The shop at the front was lined with every conceivable sort of clock, all ticking and chiming away, while my grandfather would be esconed at the counter behind tall glazed screens, eyeglass in one eye, busily engaged in cleaning a watch.

At the back and above were the living premises - quite humble but comfortable [no bathroom and an outside loo!] and a pocket handkerchief garden which was my grandmother's pride and joy. My grandfather had a contract for the maintenance and repair of clocks at some churches in villages around Northampton, and sometimes he would take my father with him. I'm sure this must have kindled a third interest which remained with my father - visiting village churches.

In many ways life in Northampton before the First World War must have still been very Dickensian. My father remembered seeing the queues of people at the bakers shops at the weekend, waiting to collect their joints and potatoes which had been taken in for roasting.

Not long before he died, he was telling us that he clearly remembered seeing Halley's comet in 1910. Had he lived until now, I'm afraid he would have been in for a big disappointment!

6. Schooling

I have a vague recollection of being shown the school which my father first attended, but cannot remember the name now. Dates of attendance must have been about 1909-1915. I have no knowledge of his performance or prowess at Primary School but presumably he won a Scholarship to enable him to go to the Grammar School.

Secondary School : Northampton Grammar School, 1915-1922. Again, regrettably, I have no detailed knowledge of his time here. Obviously he must have been successful as he won some form prizes, judging from the plates in books he owned and perhaps a Scholarship to University.

On the sporting side, I think he played rugger for the school - he certainly retained an interest in the game, and I can remember going with him to watch the Rolls-Royce team on many Saturdays in the 1950s.

7. University

Bristol University, 1922-1925, when he obtained his B.Sc.

The family were not wealthy, and sending my father to University would have posed even more problems, but apparently an elderly gentleman who was a friend of the family on my grandmother's side must have been impressed with my father's potential, and gave some financial support to my father. Even so, things were not easy, and I know that in order to save money, my father used to cycle to and from Bristol - quite a trip!

One rather amusing sidelight is that my father told my wife that once at University, his professor took him to one side and told him that he really must do something about his maths

8. First Job

I think that my father worked for a short time with Armstrong Siddeley at Coventry before being taken on by Rolls-Royce, but I know no details of this.

9. Music in my Father's Life

Music was always important in the Rubbra family. As mentioned before, his mother apparently had a lovely voice and sang in the church choir. His father was very fond of music, especially the more popular operatic music, such as Verdi. His elder brother Charles Edmund has, of course, become a well known and repected composer who has very much followed his own path in contemporary music. Both brothers received the CBE within a few years of each other.

An uncle by marriage, Will Gibson, owned a music shop in Northampton. My father was always fond of music, particularly Purcell, Handel and Bach, and especially choral music; he had a good baritone voice, and did quite a lot of singing with church choirs in oratorios, etc, when he first moved to Derby. He never learnt to play the piano, for, as he said, that was monopolised by his brother!

10. Love of the Countryside

One further abiding interest in my father's life was the countryside, and he was never happier than when exploring new country and villages, or revisiting his boyhood haunts in Northamptonshire.

11. Early Days at Rolls-Royce

These are probably more fully covered in my father's memoirs, but I will just mention two aspects which I certainly knew nothing about, but which he told my wife about when staying with us.

When my father first started at Rolls-Royce, he had to accept the low salary paid to young graduates, and this barely covered the cost of his digs. Apparently his professor at Bristol suggested that he should apply for a special grant, from a fund started at the time of the Great Exhibition in 1851. Inspired by the interest in science/engineering aroused by the Exhibition, a group of prosperous business men/scientists set up a fund to help young graduates in science/engineering during the first year or two of their employment. My father was fortunate enough to be awarded one of these special grants.

Not long after my father started work at Rolls-Royce, he was working in the testing shed, and devised some means of obtaining more accurate results of the tests. Mr Rowledge, on one of his tours of inspection, spotted this and demanded to know who was responsible for it. On being told, "Rubbra, one of the new graduates", he was silent for a bit, and then said, "Tell him to see me in my office at 11.30".

My father was busy elsewhere at the time, but when given the message, wondered if he was about to be fired. With his knees knocking, he duly went to Mr Rowledge's office, and was asked for, and gave, an explanation. After a moment Mr Rowledge said, "Pack up your things and move into the Design Office this afternoon. I need young men like you!"

Mr Rowledge's secretary was of course, Lilian Webster, who before not too long became Mrs Arthur Rubbra - which seems a good point on which to conclude.

COLIN RUBBRA
Formby
January 1986

Notes on A A Rubbra's Career at Rolls-Royce

by Donald J Pepper (Ppr)

Rbr was one of the 'second generation' engineers overlapping in years Sir Henry Royce and his team. He was among the first graduate entry and his great interest and forte was mechanical design; in the classic Royce mould.

His judgement in his field was always uniquely trusted. He was always approachable and modest and never made an enemy. Every part of a piston engine needed Rbr and very many parts of a gas turbine needed him too.

He accepted an invitation to continue after retirement as a consultant to the Company on design problems in the aero, car and nuclear fields.

Outline of Rbr's Career

1925   He joined Rolls-Royce on 13th July 1925 in the Experimental Department under Hs. His first job was as an Assistant Tester, Check No 2392 and he was paid £1 0s 0d per week. On joining he was given a testimonial by a Mr W H Gibson, Piano and Music Dealer of Northampton. Dated 17th July 1925, it reads:

> "I have known A Rubbra the whole of his life and have always found him reliable in every way, steady industrious in his studies and ambitious. I am pleased to be able to testify to his general character."

In the Experimental Department Rbr worked particularly on aero engines, among them the 'X' configuration Eagle XVI and the early prototypes of the 'F' engine (later named the Kestrel) and the 'H' engine (which became the Buzzard).

1927   On 10 October 1927 Rbr was transferred to Staff, Check No 1025S as a Designer under A J Rowledge (Rg). Then he worked on the Kestrel, Buzzard and 'R' engines and was particularly involved in the design of the evaporatively cooled Goshawk, the Merlin and Vulture. On 28 April 1928 he was transferred to Monthly Staff.

1934   Continuing in the duties just described Rbr was appointed Assistant Chief Designer in 1934.

1940   On 20 July 1940 he was appointed Chief Designer Aero Engines at the same time that Lov was made Development and Research Engineer. This was when Colonel Barrington, who had been Design Office Manager since Rg's retirement, was sent to USA on the Packard Merlin exercise.

Miss Griffin became Rbr's secretary during the year.

In this capacity Rbr did vital design work on the various marks of Merlin, including early civil versions and played a big part in the design of the Griffon aero engine.

In 1943 he became involved in the design of the 46H24 twin crank horizontally opposed Eagle piston engine and, more significantly, in design work on the Welland, the company's first production turbine aero engine.

1944   He was appointed Assisant Chief Engineer in 1944, ,and during the year worked on such engines as the B.37 Derwent. Mechanical design work on the Dart propjet followed in 1945 and on the Nene in 1946. Later in 1948, he played a significant part in the birth and development of the Avon turbojet. With Lov he was responsible for combining variable swirl with compressor bleed and he was also responsible for the hairpin root compressor disc design. This helped overcome the problems previously experienced of compressors going out of balance when running. Hairpin roots are still used today.

1951   In 1951 Rbr was appointed Deputy Chief Engineer.

1954   On 14 December 1954 Rbr was appointed to the Company Board as Technical Director - Aero. During the period following this the Tyne and Conway were designed and developed.

1958   On the creation of the Divisional Boards, Rbr was appointed to the AED Board on 21 July 1958 and his Main Board duties widened to be Technical Director - All divisions.

In this post, Rbr concerned himself with both the Company's committed projects and investigating potential new fields and types of prime movers and power generators. He was responsible for investigating potential improvements in the gas turbine cycle efficiency. He kept a close interest in the work of the Advanced Research Laboratories in fields such as the development of composite materials, was involved in product failure investigation and in particular was closely associated with the Company's work in the nuclear field.

1961   Rbr was awarded the CBE.

1965   Rbr was responsible for the investigation of the Company Museum Project.

1966   On 15 February 1966 Rbr relinquished his Technical Directorship for health reasons but continued as the Company's Chief Technical Advisor.

His work included investigations in the field of Wankel engines and Free Piston engine, failures investigation and railway traction.

1968   Earlier in the year he relinquished his Vice Chairmanship of Rolls-Royce and Associates. He retired from Rolls-Royce Ltd   in October 1968, but remained as a consultant.

1971   When the Company was confronted with the problem of the RB211 he joined a team led by Sir Stanley Hooker to provide technical advice to the Engineering Department in dealing with major difficulties and thus contributed to the entry of the engine into service.

DON PEPPER